200 Classic
CHESS
PUZZLES

200 Classic
CHESS
PUZZLES

Edited
by
Martin Greif

 Sterling Publishing Co., Inc. New York

Library of Congress Cataloging-in-Publication Data

200 classic chess puzzles / edited by Martin Greif.
      p.   cm.
  Includes index.
  ISBN 0-8069-0462-3
  1. Chess problems. I. Greif, Martin, [*date*]. II. Title: Two
hundred classic chess puzzles.
GV1451.A16   1993
794.1'7—dc20   93–14610
                                      CIP

Designed by John Murphy
Typeset by Upper Case Limited, Cork, Ireland.

10 9 8 7 6 5 4 3

Published by Sterling Publishing Company, Inc.
387 Park Avenue South, New York, N.Y. 10016
© 1993 Martin Greif
Distributed in Canada by Sterling Publishing
c/o Canadian Manda Group, P.O. Box 920, Station U
Toronto, Ontario, Canada M8Z 5P9
Distributed in Great Britain and Europe by Cassell PLC
Villiers House, 41/47 Strand, London WC2N 5JE, England
Distributed in Australia by Capricorn Link Ltd.
P.O. Box 665, Lane Cove, NSW 2066
Manufactured in the United States of America
All rights reserved

Sterling ISBN 0-8069-0462-3

CONTENTS

INTRODUCTION

The object in chess, of course, is to trap, or checkmate, the opponent's King into a check from which it cannot escape, thus bringing the game to a victorious conclusion. *200 Classic Chess Puzzles* is a collection of gripping, grueling, and teeth-grating end games in which a checkmate, or mate, is required in two, three, four, or more moves. Shown the illustration of a board with chess pieces in fixed positions, it's up to you to determine how to take the King in a given number of moves. What's more, if you're to solve the puzzle successfully, you have to take the part of both players, seeing the game from the point of view of both Black and White. In these riveting chess puzzles, you'll be forced to play the end game both aggressively and defensively, keeping the pieces of both opponents concentrated in logical cooperation until you can say with certainty, "the King is dead," the literal meaning of the Persian *shāh māt*, from which the term "checkmate" derives.

200 Classic Chess Puzzles is intended for both the player with only an elementary understanding of the game and for the more advanced player who wishes to test his skill. Since the end game is the most important phase of chess, and a good end-game player can vanquish the opening or middle-game specialist, concentrating on these brilliant puzzles will not only provide hours of brain-teasing fun, but may help you to be a better end-game player and enable you to enjoy the challenging endings and therefore chess to the full. Included in the puzzles are Pawn endings, Rook and Pawn endings, Queen endings, Queen and

Pawn endings, Rook and Pawn endings, and minor piece endings. *200 Classic Chess Puzzles*, all culled from award-winning chess problems from the past, forces you to play end games that are full of excitement, color, brilliance, and subtlety. And, if you're stumped, or even if you're not, the solutions appear in the back of the book.

A word or two about these solutions is in order. First, the shorthand used to describe chess play in these pages is a modified form of standard Descriptive (or English) Notation, with a dash (—) indicating moves (e.g. P—K4) and an *x* indicating captures (e.g. Q x B). Such abbreviations as *ch*, *db ch*, and *dis ch* (check, double check, and discovers [reveals] check) are obvious, while the beginner may, perhaps, need to be reminded that *e.p.* stands for a capture *en passant*.

Second, since many of the puzzles allow for *more* than one solution, alternative solutions — frequently more than one — are offered. These alternative solutions and moves are indicated by asterisks (*, **, or ***).

Finally, several of the puzzles are not only tricky in their own right, but tricky by design — that is, while the correct solution might call for, say, four moves, you might in fact give mate in only three. The challenge lies in finding the *stipulated* number of moves, even if there is an easier way! With this caveat in mind, enjoy these 200 classic chess challenges to the full.

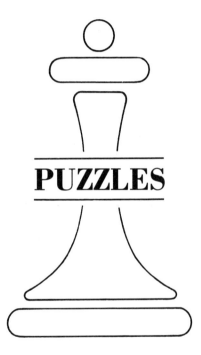

PUZZLES

PUZZLE No. 1
Black

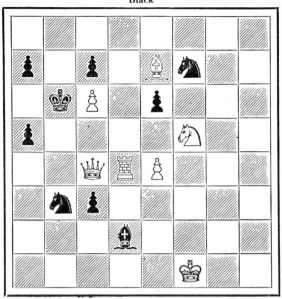

White
White to play and mate in three moves.

PUZZLE No. 2
Black

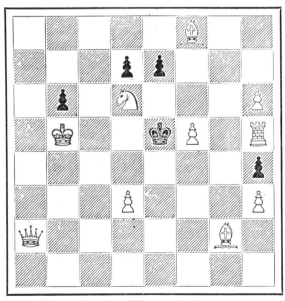

White
White to play and mate in two moves.

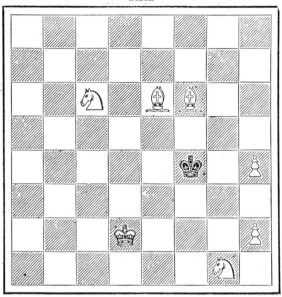

White
White to play and mate in three moves.

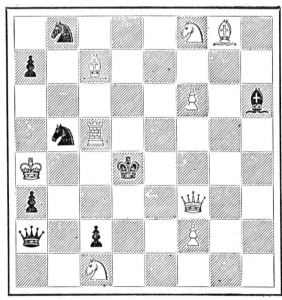

White
White to play and mate in two moves.

PUZZLE No. 5
Black

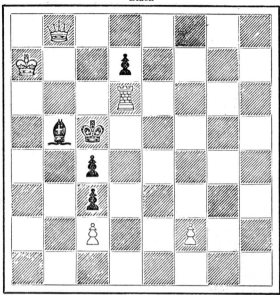

White
White to play and mate in three moves.

PUZZLE No. 6
Black

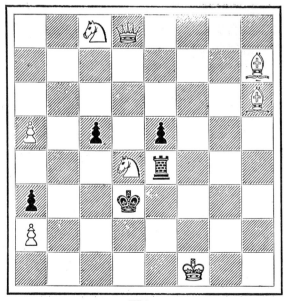

White
White to play and mate in three moves.

PUZZLE No. 7
Black

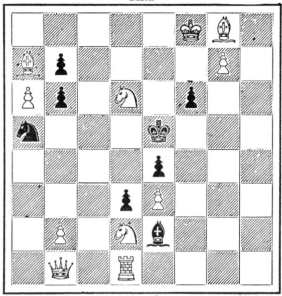

White
White to play and mate in three moves.

PUZZLE No. 8
Black

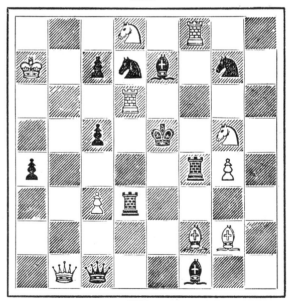

White
White to play and mate in two moves.

14

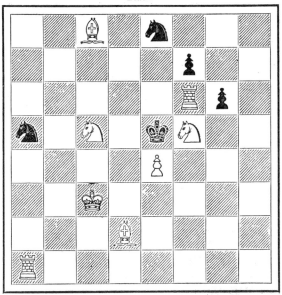

White
White to play and mate in two moves.

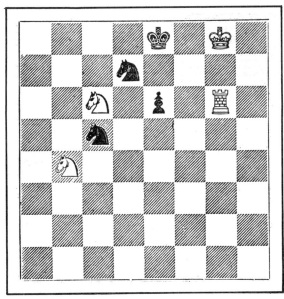

White
White to play and mate in three moves.

15

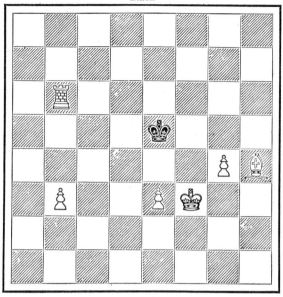

White
White to play and mate in three moves.

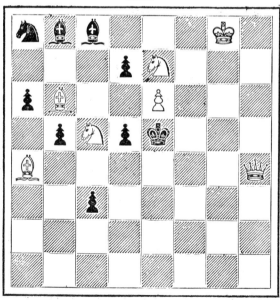

White
White to play and mate in three moves.

16

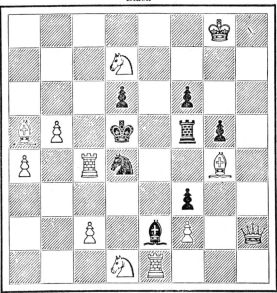

White
White to play and mate in two moves.

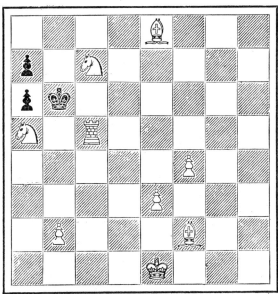

White
White to play and mate in three moves.

PUZZLE No. 15
Black

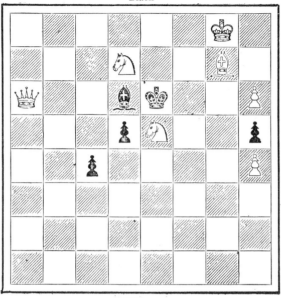

White
White to play and mate in four moves.

PUZZLE No. 16
Black

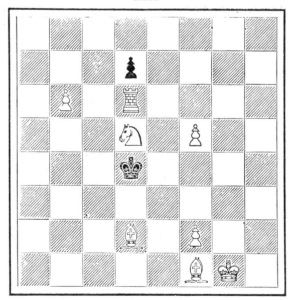

White
White to play and mate in three moves.

PUZZLE No. 17
Black

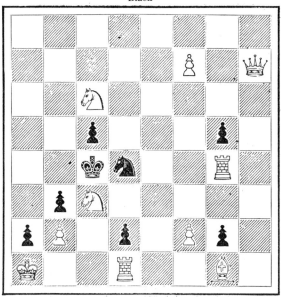

White
White to play and mate in three moves.

PUZZLE No. 18
Black

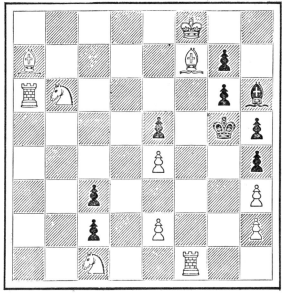

White
White to play and mate in three moves.

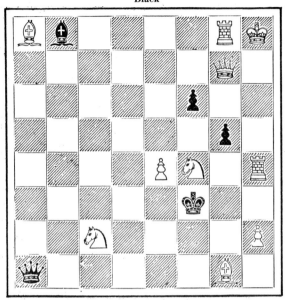

White
White to play and mate in two moves.

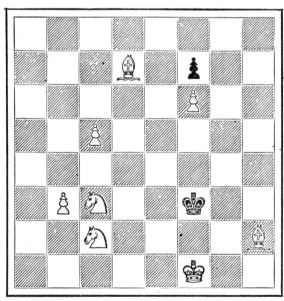

White
White to play and mate in three moves.

PUZZLE No. 21
Black

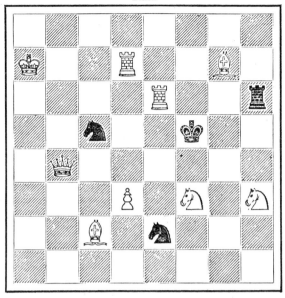

White
White to play and mate in two moves.

PUZZLE No. 22
Black

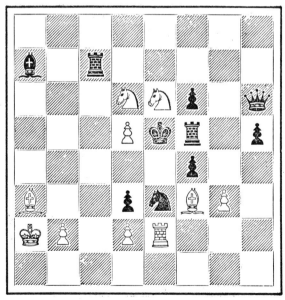

White
White to play and mate in two moves.

PUZZLE No. 23
Black

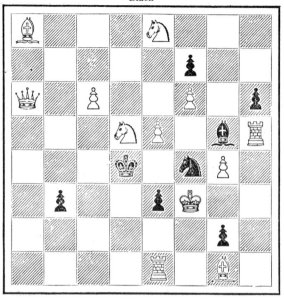

White
White to play and mate in three moves.

PUZZLE No. 24
Black

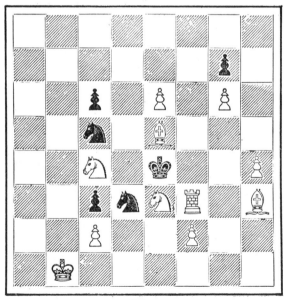

White
White to play and mate in four moves.

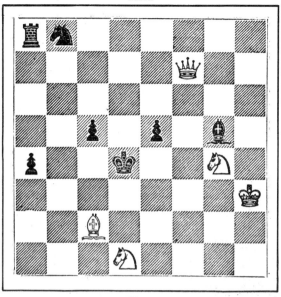

White
White to play and mate in four moves.

PUZZLE No. 26
Black

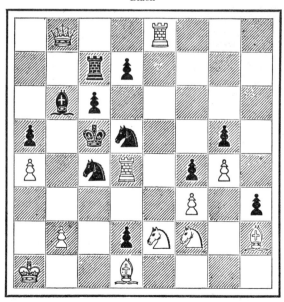

White
White to play and mate in two moves.

PUZZLE No. 27
Black

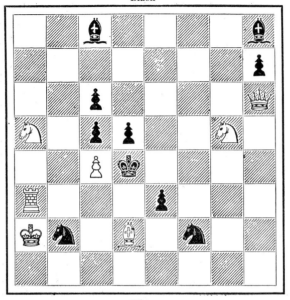

White
White to play and mate in two moves.

PUZZLE No. 28
Black

White
White to play and mate in three moves.

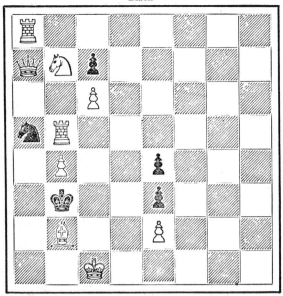

White
White to play and mate in two moves.

PUZZLE No. 30
Black

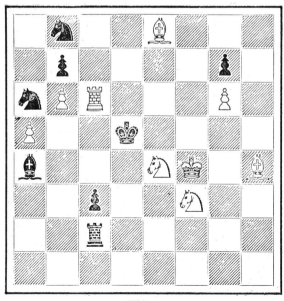

White
White to play and mate in three moves.

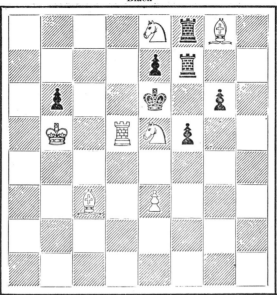

White
White to play and mate in three moves.

White
White to play and mate in three moves.

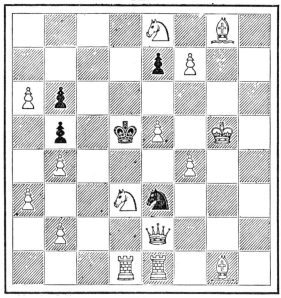

White
White to play and mate in two moves.

White
White to play and mate in three moves.

PUZZLE No. 35
Black

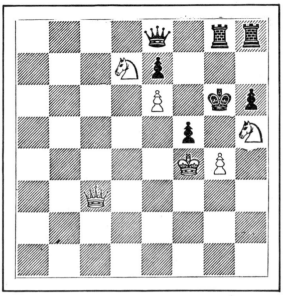

White
White to play and mate in four moves.

PUZZLE No. 36
Black

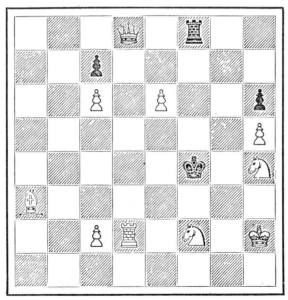

White
White to play and mate in two moves.

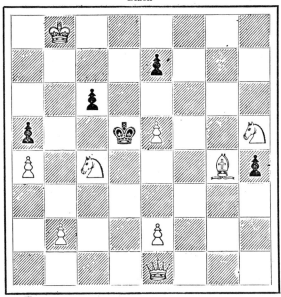

White
White to play and mate in three moves.

___

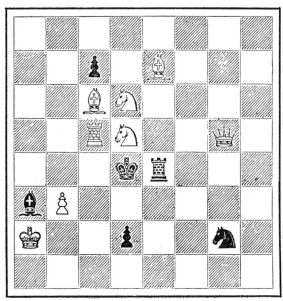

White
White to play and mate in three moves.

PUZZLE No. 39
Black

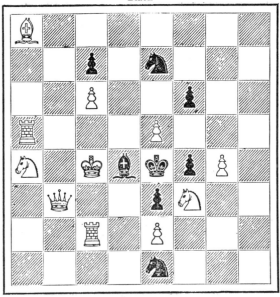

White
White to play and mate in two moves.

PUZZLE No. 40
Black

White
White to play and mate in three moves.

Black

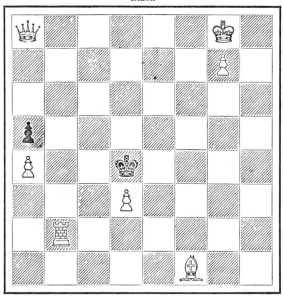

White
White to play and mate in three moves.

PUZZLE No. 42
Black

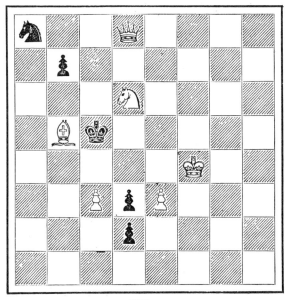

White
White to play and mate in three moves.

PUZZLE No. 43
Black

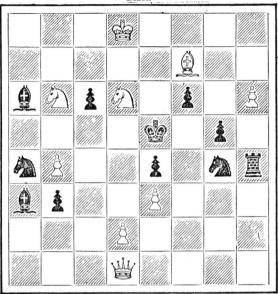

White
White to play and mate in three moves.

PUZZLE No. 44
Black

White
White to play and mate in three moves.

PUZZLE No. 45
Black

White
White to play and mate in three moves.

PUZZLE No. 46
Black

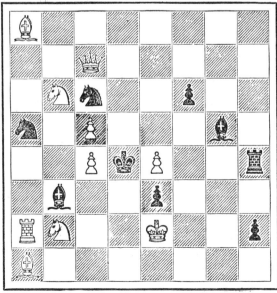

White
White to play and mate in two moves.

33

PUZZLE No. 47
Black

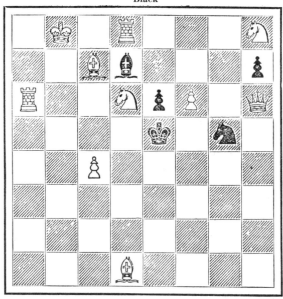

White
White to play and mate in two moves.

PUZZLE No. 48
Black

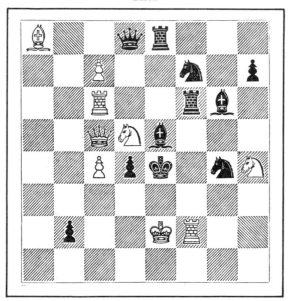

White
White to play and mate in five moves.

White
White to play and mate in three moves.

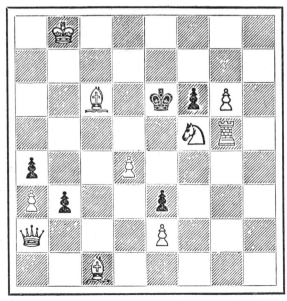

White
White to play and mate in three moves.

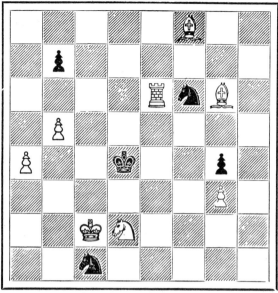

White
White to play and mate in three moves.

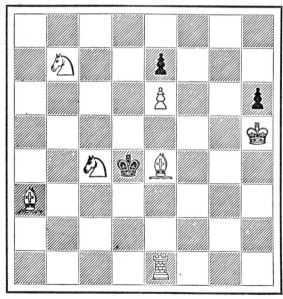

White
White to play and mate in three moves.

PUZZLE No. 53
Black

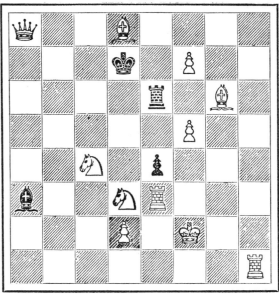

White
White to play and mate in two moves.

PUZZLE No. 54
Black

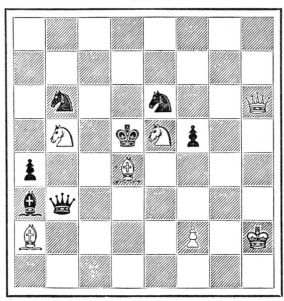

White
White to play and mate in three moves.

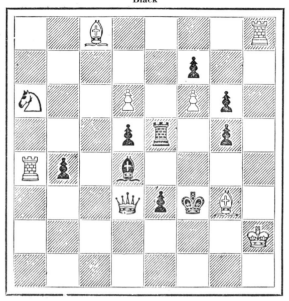

White
White to play and mate in three moves.

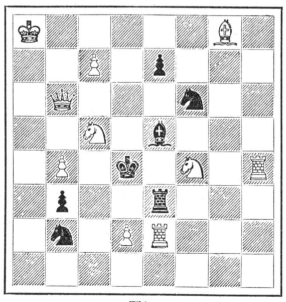

White
White to play and mate in two moves.

PUZZLE No. 57
Black

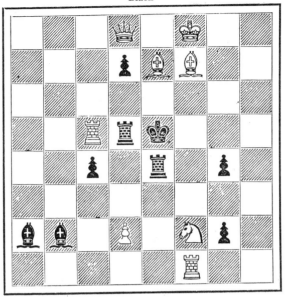

White
White to play and mate in two moves.

PUZZLE No. 58
Black

White
White to play and mate in two moves.

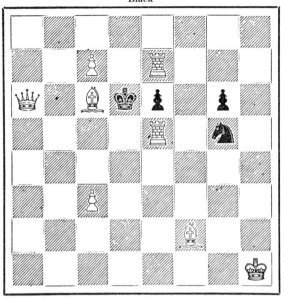

White
White to play and mate in two moves.

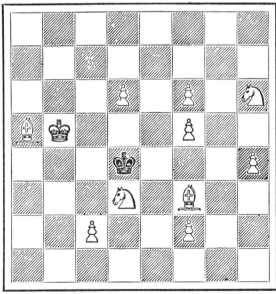

White
White to play and mate in three moves.

PUZZLE No. 61
Black

White
White to play and mate in four moves.

PUZZLE No. 62
Black

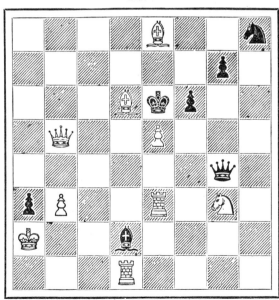

White
White to play and mate in two moves.

41

PUZZLE No. 63
Black

White
White to play and mate in three moves.

PUZZLE No. 64
Black

White
White to play and mate in three moves.

PUZZLE No. 65
Black

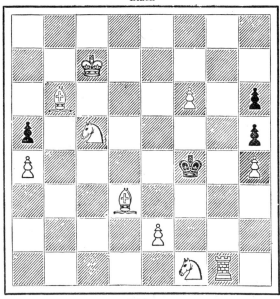

White
White to play and mate in three moves.

PUZZLE No. 66
Black

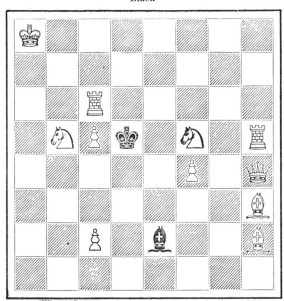

White
White to play and mate in two moves.

43

PUZZLE No. 67
Black

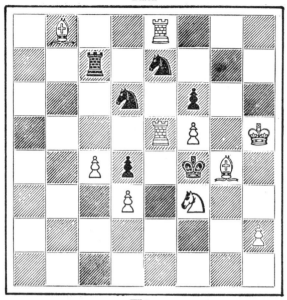

White
White to play and mate in two moves.

PUZZLE No. 68
Black

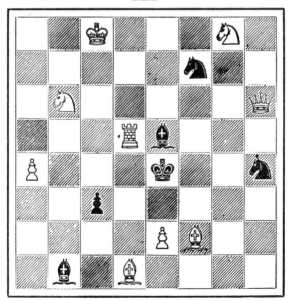

White
White to play and mate in three moves.

44

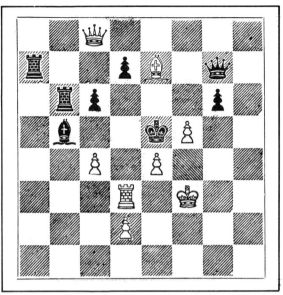

White
White to play and mate in four moves.

White
White to play and mate in four moves.

White
White to play and mate in four moves.

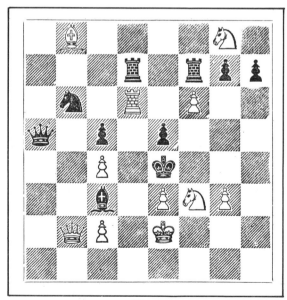

White
White to play and mate in five moves.

PUZZLE No. 73
Black

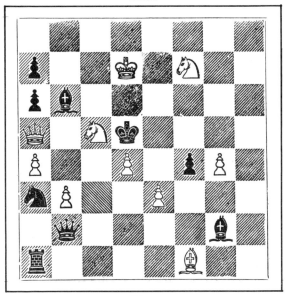

White
White to play and mate in five moves.

PUZZLE No. 74
Black

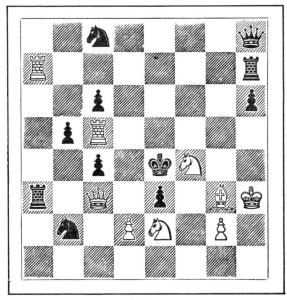

White
White to play and mate in four moves.

47

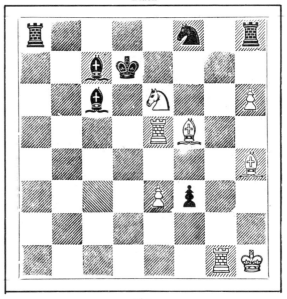

White
White to play and mate in four moves.

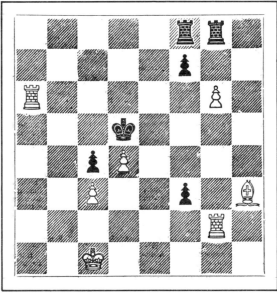

White
White to play and mate in four moves.

PUZZLE No. 77
Black

White
White to play and mate in four moves.

PUZZLE No. 78
Black

White
White to play and mate in five moves.

49

White
White to play and mate in four moves.

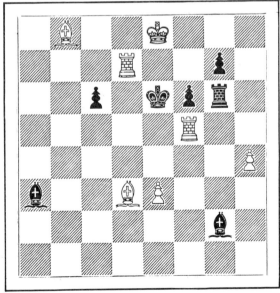

White
White to play and mate in four moves.

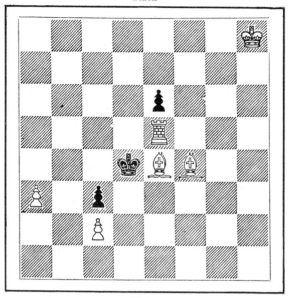

White
White to play and mate in four moves.

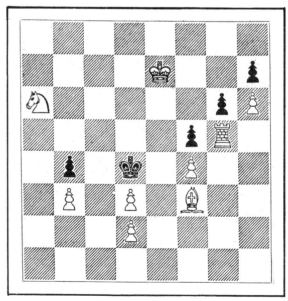

White
White to play and mate in four moves.

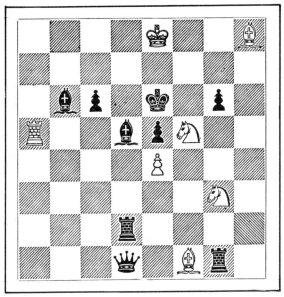

White
White to play and mate in four moves.

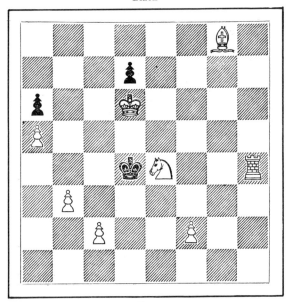

White
White to play and mate in five moves.

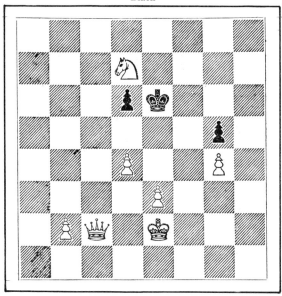

White
White to play and mate in four moves.

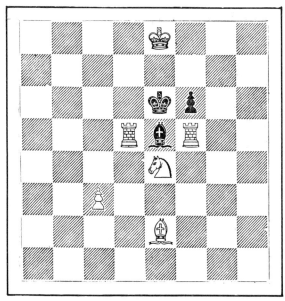

White
White to play and mate in four moves.

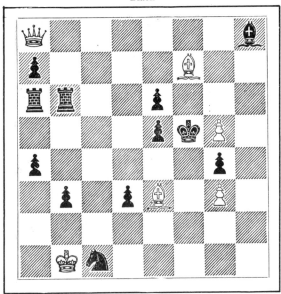

White
White to play and mate in five moves.

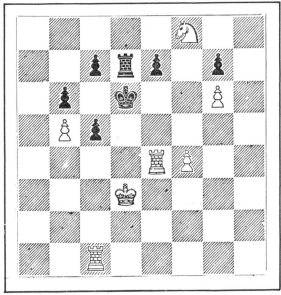

White
White to play and mate in four moves.

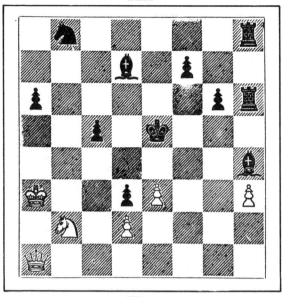

White
White to play and mate in four moves.

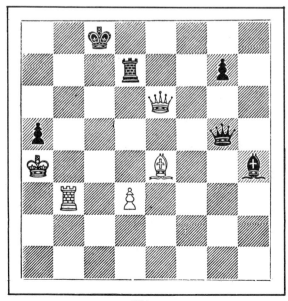

White
White to play and mate in four moves.

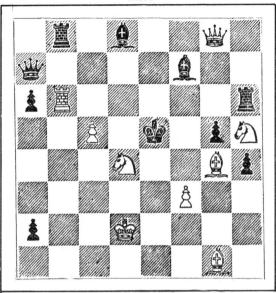

White
White to play and mate in five moves.

White
White to play and mate in five moves.

PUZZLE No. 93
Black

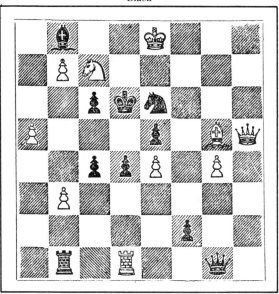

White
White to play and mate in five moves.

PUZZLE No. 94
Black

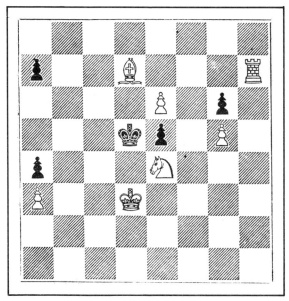

White
White to play and mate in four moves.

57

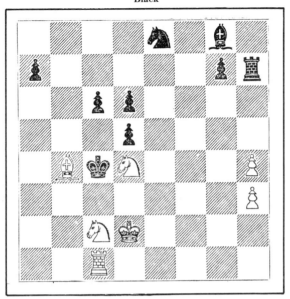

White
White to play and mate in four moves.

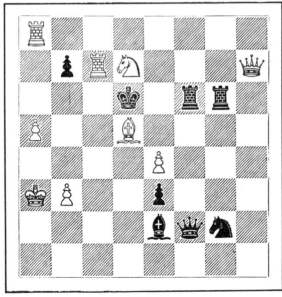

White
White to play and mate in four moves.

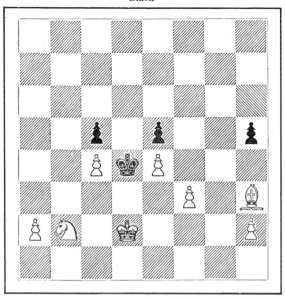

White
White to play and mate in five moves.

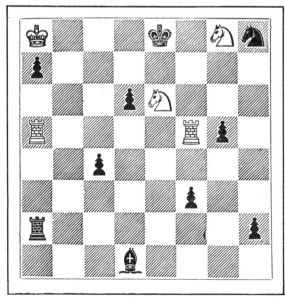

White
White to play and mate in three moves.

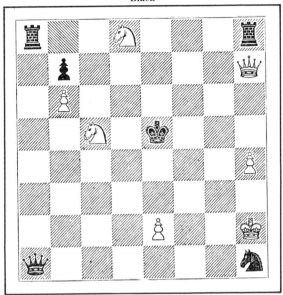

White
White to play and mate in six moves.

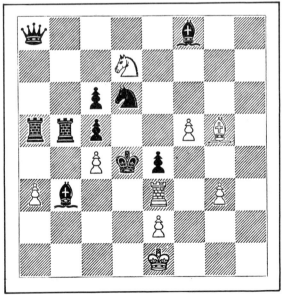

White
White to play and mate in four moves.

PUZZLE No. 101
Black

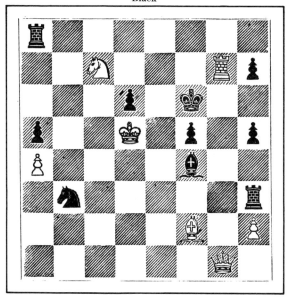

White
White to play and mate in four moves.

PUZZLE No. 102
Black

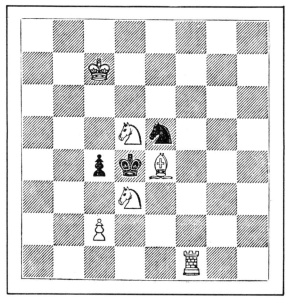

White
White to play and mate in four moves.

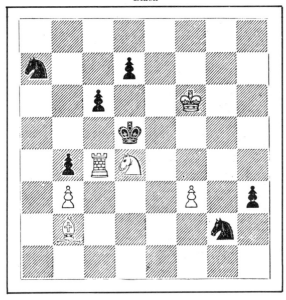

White
White to play and mate in five moves.

White
White to play and mate in five moves.

PUZZLE No. 105
Black

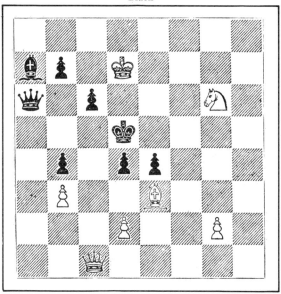

White
White to play and mate in four moves.

PUZZLE No. 106
Black

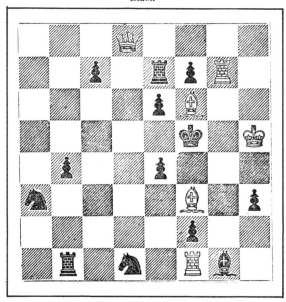

White
White to play and mate in four moves.

63

PUZZLE No. 107
Black

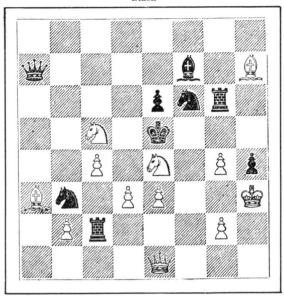

White
White to play and mate in four moves.

PUZZLE No. 108
Black

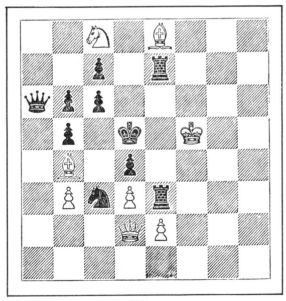

White
White to play and mate in five moves.

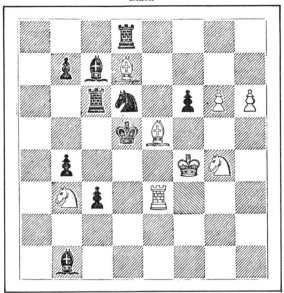

White
White to play and mate in six moves.

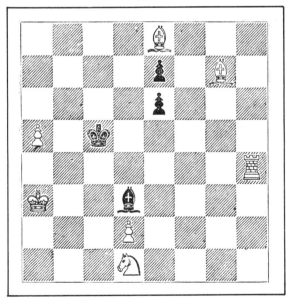

White
White to play and mate in four moves.

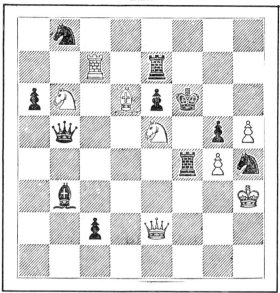

White
White to play and mate in four moves.

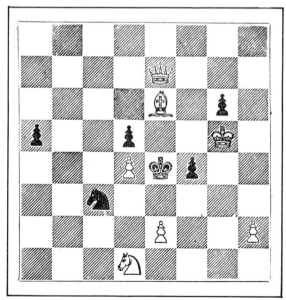

White
White to play and mate in three moves.

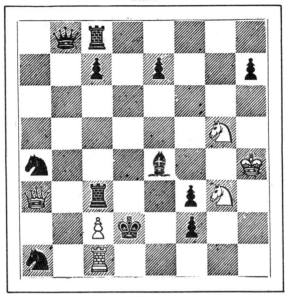

White
White to play and mate in five moves.

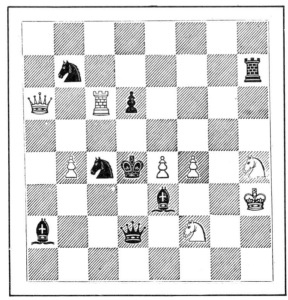

White
White to play and mate in five moves.

White
White to play and mate in seven moves.

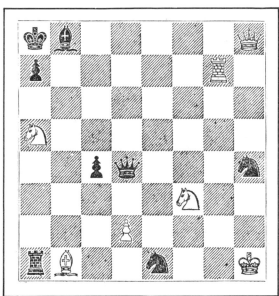

White
White to play and mate in four moves.

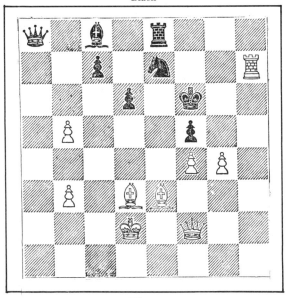

White
White to play and mate in five moves.

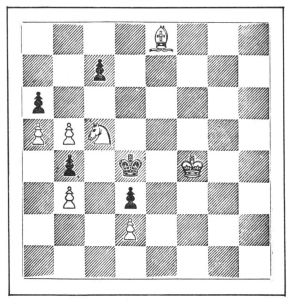

White
White to play and mate in five moves.

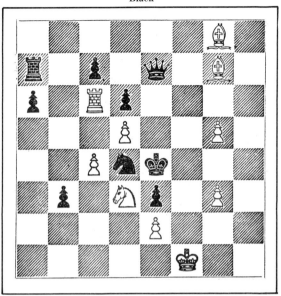

White
White to play and mate in six moves.

White
White to play and mate in three moves.

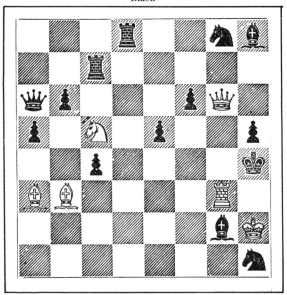

White
White to play and mate in five moves.

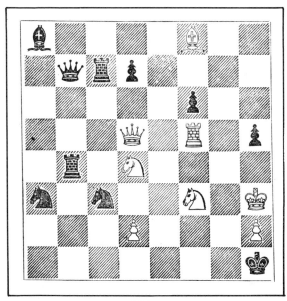

White
White to play and mate in five moves.

PUZZLE No. 123
Black

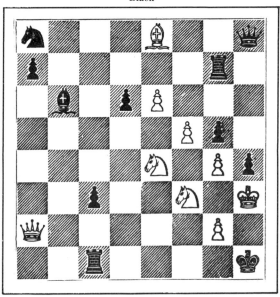

White
White to play and mate in five moves.

PUZZLE No. 124
Black

White
White to play and mate in five moves.

72

PUZZLE No. 125
Black

White
White to play and mate in five moves.

PUZZLE No. 126
Black

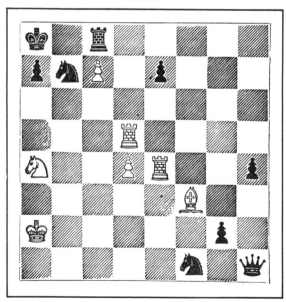

White
White to play and mate in four moves.

PUZZLE No. 127
Black

White
White to play and mate in five moves.

PUZZLE No. 128
Black

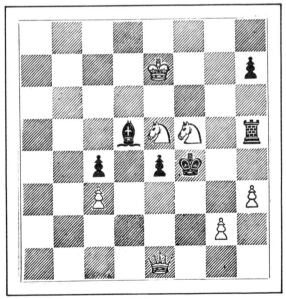

White
White to play and mate in three moves.

74

White
White to play and mate in four moves.

White
White to play and mate in three moves.

White
White to play and mate in four moves.

White
White to play and mate in three moves.

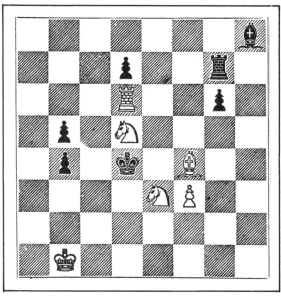

White
White to play and mate in three moves.

White
White to play and mate in three moves.

White
White to play and mate in five moves.

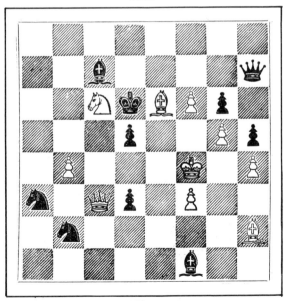

White
White to play and mate in five moves.

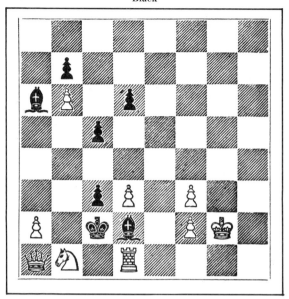

White
White to play and mate in four moves.

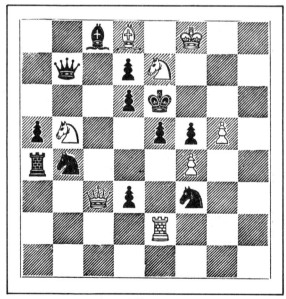

White
White to play and mate in four moves.

PUZZLE No. 139
Black

White
White to play and mate in three moves.

PUZZLE No. 140
Black

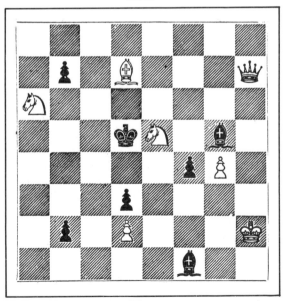

White
White to play and mate in four moves.

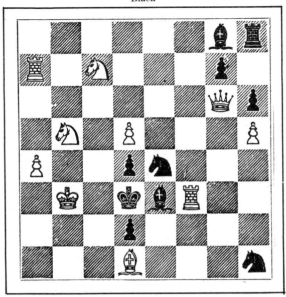

White
White to play and mate in four moves.

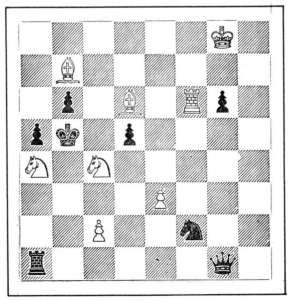

White
White to play and mate in three moves.

PUZZLE No. 143
Black

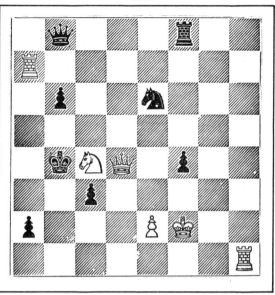

White
White to play and mate in six moves.

PUZZLE No. 144
Black

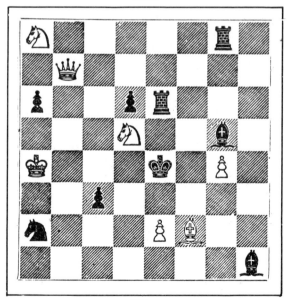

White
White to play and mate in four moves.

PUZZLE No. 145
Black

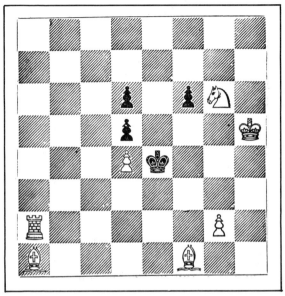

White
White to play and mate in three moves.

PUZZLE No. 146
Black

White
White to play and mate in four moves.

PUZZLE No. 147
Black

White
White to play and mate in four moves.

PUZZLE No. 148
Black

White
White to play and mate in four moves.

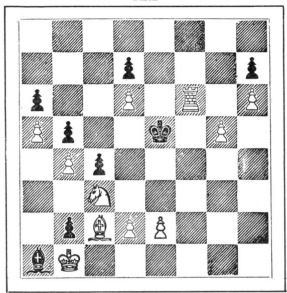

White
White to play and mate in four moves.

White
White to play and mate in three moves.

PUZZLE No. 151
Black

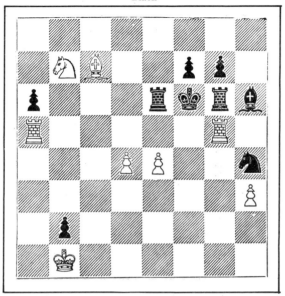

White
White to play and mate in five moves.

PUZZLE No. 152
Black

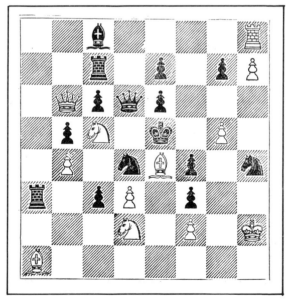

White
White to play and mate in five moves.

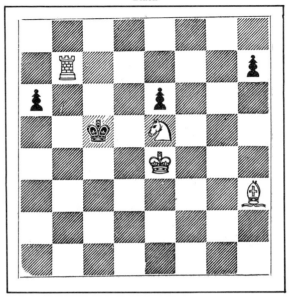

White
White to play and mate in five moves.

PUZZLE No. 154
Black

White
White to play and mate in three moves.

PUZZLE No. 155
Black

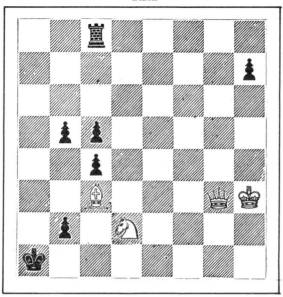

White
White to play and mate in three moves.

PUZZLE No. 156
Black

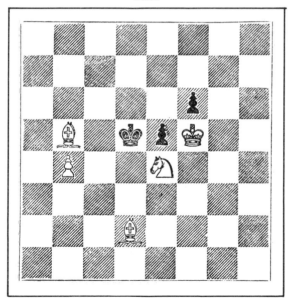

White
White to play and mate in five moves.

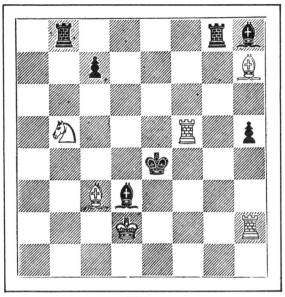

White
White to play and mate in three moves.

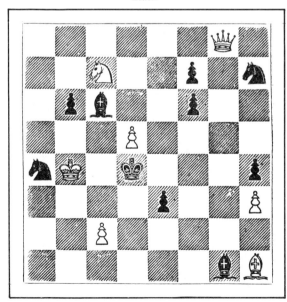

White
White to play and mate in five moves.

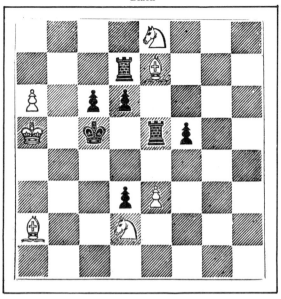

White
White to play and mate in four moves.

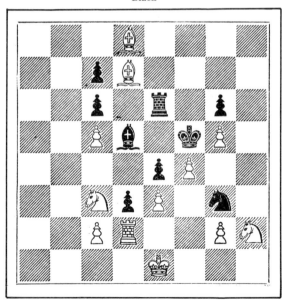

White
White to play and mate in four moves.

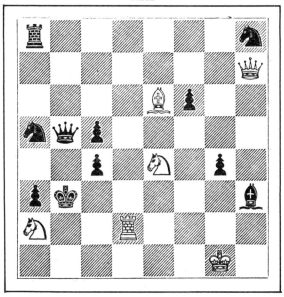

White
White to play and mate in three moves.

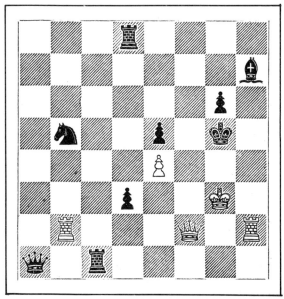

White
White to play and mate in five moves.

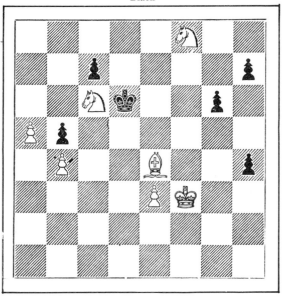

White
White to play and mate in four moves.

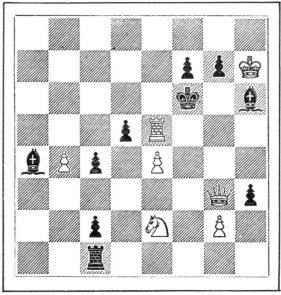

White
White to play and mate in three moves.

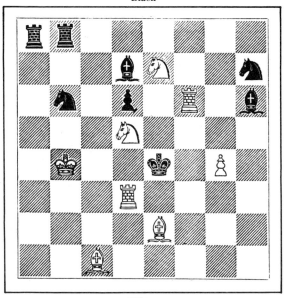

White
White to play and mate in four moves.

PUZZLE No. 166
Black

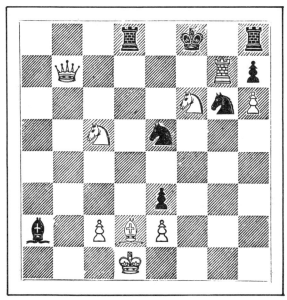

White
White to play and mate in three moves.

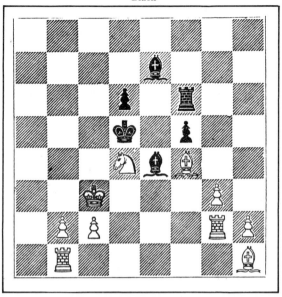

White
White to play and mate in four moves.

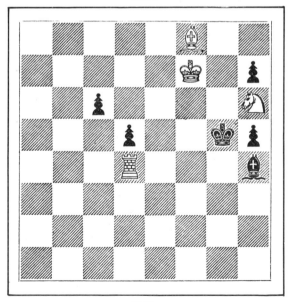

White
White to play and mate in four moves.

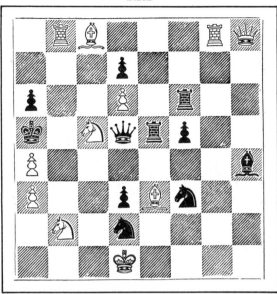

White
White to play and mate in four moves.

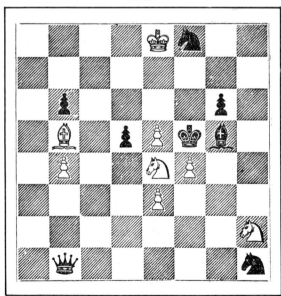

White
White to play and mate in five moves.

PUZZLE No. 171
Black

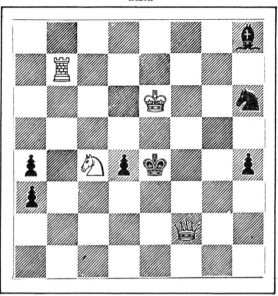

White
White to play and mate in three moves.

PUZZLE No. 172
Black

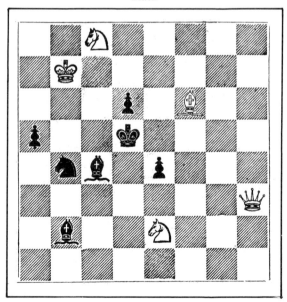

White
White to play and mate in four moves.

PUZZLE No. 173
Black

White
White to play and mate in five moves.

PUZZLE No. 174
Black

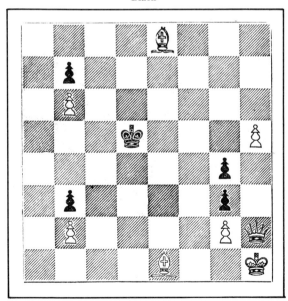

White
White to play and mate in four moves.

97

White
White to play and mate in four moves.

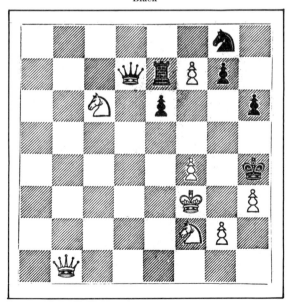

White
White to play and mate in five moves.

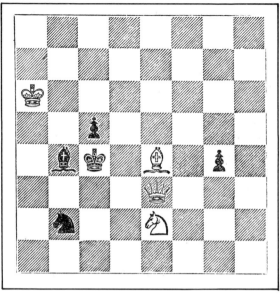

White
White to play and mate in three moves.

PUZZLE No. 178
Black

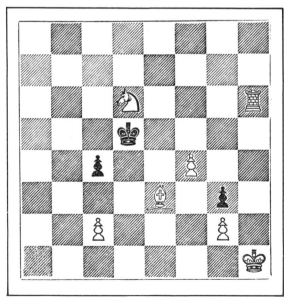

White
White to play and mate in five moves.

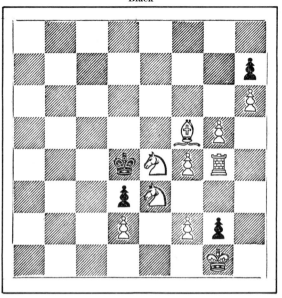

White
White to play and mate in four moves.

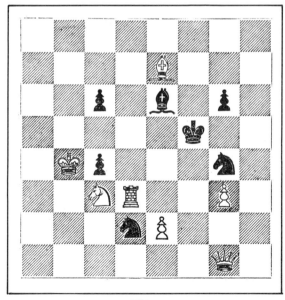

White
White to play and mate in four moves.

PUZZLE No. 181
Black

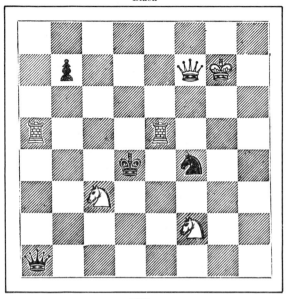

White
White to play and mate in three moves.

PUZZLE No. 182
Black

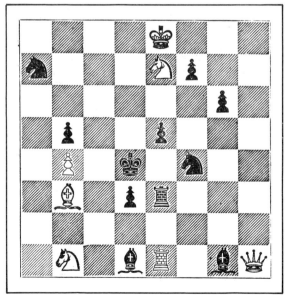

White
White to play and mate in three moves.

White
White to play and mate in four moves.

White
White to play and mate in three moves.

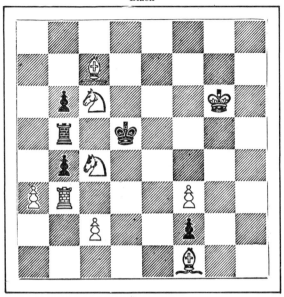

White
White to play and mate in three moves.

White
White to play and mate in four moves.

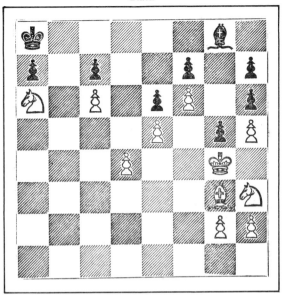

White
White to play and mate in five moves.

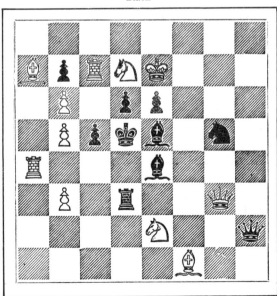

White
White to play and mate in six moves.

PUZZLE No. 189
Black

White
White to play and mate in three moves.

PUZZLE No. 190
Black

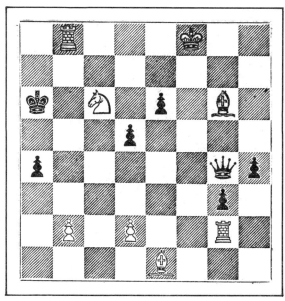

White
White to play and mate in five moves.

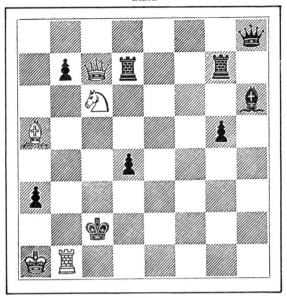

White
White to play and mate in three moves.

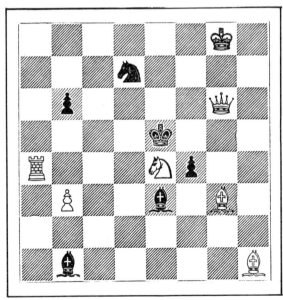

White
White to play and mate in three moves.

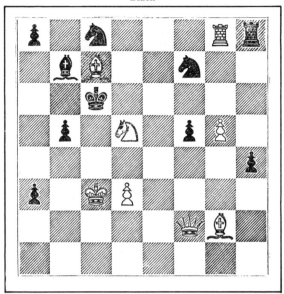

White
White to play and mate in four moves.

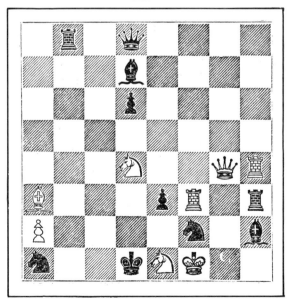

White
White to play and mate in four moves.

White
White to play and mate in three moves.

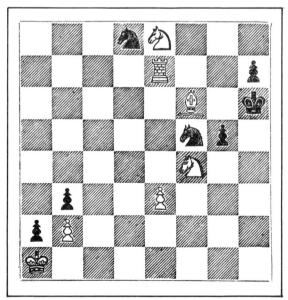

White
White to play and mate in five moves.

PUZZLE No. 197
Black

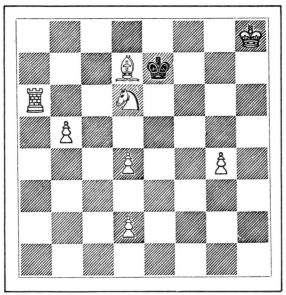

White
White to play and mate in four moves.

PUZZLE No. 198
Black

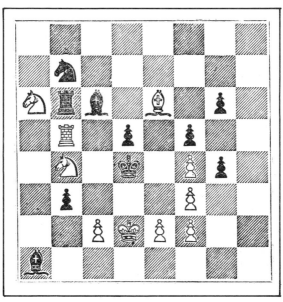

White
White to play and mate in four moves.

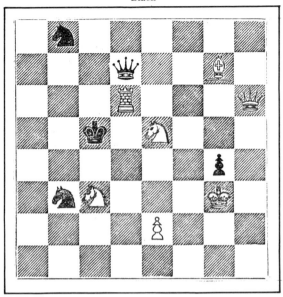

White
White to play and mate in three moves.

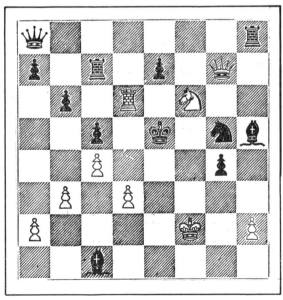

White
White to play and mate in fourteen moves.

SOLUTIONS

PUZZLE No. 1

White	Black
1. R—Q8	Kt x R*
2. Kt—Q6	Any move
3. Q, B, or Kt mates accordingly	

* The variations are obvious.

•

PUZZLE No. 2

White	Black
1. Q—KB2	Any move
2. Mates accordingly	

•

PUZZLE No. 3

White	Black
1. B—QKt2	K— K5
2. B—Q1	K—B5
3. K—Q3 dis ch	

•

PUZZLE No. 4

White	Black
1. B—Q5	Any move
2. Mates accordingly	

•

PUZZLE No. 5

White	Black
1. P—KB4	B—B3*
2. R—Q5 ch	K or B x R
3. Q mates	

* If Black plays 1. K—Kt5, then 2. R—QR6, etc.

•

PUZZLE No. 6

White	Black
1. Q—KKt5	QBP x Kt*
2. Q—Kt8	K—B6 or B7
3. Q—QKt3. Mate	

* If Black plays 1. K—B5, White continues with 2. Kt—Kt6 ch; if 1. K x Kt, then 2. Q—Q2 ch; if 1. K—B6, then 2. Q—Q2 ch; and if 1. K x Kt, then 2. Q—Kt3 ch, mating on the third move in every case.

•

PUZZLE No. 7

White	Black
1. Q—B2	P—KB4*
2. Q—B8	Any move
3. Q or B mates accordingly	

* If Black plays 1. P x P, White continues with 2. Q—QB6, if 1. B moves, then 2. K from Q2—QB4 ch; if 1. P x Q, then 2. Kt—KB3 ch; if 1. K x Kt, then 2. B—Kt8 ch, mating on the third move in every case.

•

PUZZLE No. 8

White	Black
1. B—Kt3	Any move
2. Mates accordingly	

•

PUZZLE No. 9

White	Black
1. R—K1	Any move
2. Mates accordingly	

•

PUZZLE No. 10

WHITE	BLACK
1. R x KP ch	Kt x R
2. Kt—Q5	Any move
3. Kt mates	

•

PUZZLE No. 11

WHITE	BLACK
1. B—B2	K moves
2. K—B4	K moves
3. P—K4. Mate	

•

PUZZLE No. 12

WHITE	BLACK
1. B—R5	K—Q3*
2. Q—B4 ch	K x Kt
3. Q mates	

* If Black plays 1. P x B, then 2. Q—Kt3, ch; if 1. P—Kt5, then 2. Kt—Kt6 ch, mating accordingly.

•

PUZZLE No. 13

WHITE	BLACK
1. Q—R7	Any move
2. Mates accordingly	

•

PUZZLE No. 14

WHITE	BLACK
1. B—KR4	K x R
2. B—Q8	Any move
3. Kt (either) mates accordingly	

•

PUZZLE No. 15

WHITE	BLACK
1. Kt—QKt6	K—B4*
2. Kt x QP	B x Kt
3. Q—KKt6 ch	K x Q
4. Kt—K7. Mate	

* If Black plays 1. B—QB2, 1. B x Kt, 1. B—Kt1 or R6, or 1. K—K2, White continues with 2. Q—B8, mating in two more moves. If, in the main variation, Black plays 2. K—K3, the answer is 3. Q—B8 ch: if 2. K—K5 then 3. Q x P ch, and if 2. P—B6 then 3. Q—B1 ch, mating in each case on the fourth move.
NOTE: Puzzle No. 15 is a composition of more than ordinary difficulty. In addition to the correct solution above, there are other "seemingly possible" solutions so that it is desirable to append a short analysis showing the correct defenses in each case:

The most important of these suggested solutions are 1. Kt—KB6, 1. Kt—QB5 ch, 1. Q—B8, and 1. Q—Kt6. To 1. Kt—KB6, Black has a good answer in Kt x K, Black's subsequent moves presenting no difficulty after the capture. If White plays Kt—QB5 ch, Black's best reply is K—B4, when the following are the most likely moves on both sides: 2. Q—B6 ch, K—B5; 3. Q—KR3, B x Kt at K4, and there is no mate next move, the White P at KR6 preventing B being played to that square. 1. Q—B8 is also met by 1. K—B4; after which if K is played to B5, discovering check, we have the position occurring in the last variation, and if nothing else K escapes easily. The answer to Q—Kt6 is 1. P—QB6; and should White continue with 2. Q—KB2 then 2. B x Kt defers the mate beyond the fourth move. Such obviously crude efforts as Kt x QBP, and a so-called mate in three moves by promoting P at KR6 to royal rank, call for no comment.

PUZZLE No. 16

WHITE	BLACK
1. P—B4	K—B4*
2. Kt—K7	K x R
3. B mates	

* If Black plays 1. K—K5, White continues with 2. Kt—B6, etc.

•

PUZZLE No. 17

WHITE	BLACK
1. Q—QKt1	P x Q (a Q ch)*
2. K x Q	K moves
3. Kt mates	

* There is also a solution to this problem commencing 1. Kt x Kt.

•

PUZZLE No. 18

WHITE	BLACK
1. R—Q1	P x R (a Q)*
2. Kt—Q5	Any move
3. R or B mates accordingly	

* If 1.K—B5, then 2. Kt—Q5 ch, etc.

•

PUZZLE No. 19

WHITE	BLACK
1. Q—QR7	Any move
2. Mates accordingly	

•

PUZZLE No. 20

WHITE	BLACK
1. Kt—Kt1	K—K5
2. B—Q6	K moves
3. Kt or B mates accordingly	

PUZZLE No. 21

WHITE	BLACK
1. B—Q1	Any move
2. Mates accordingly	

•

PUZZLE No. 22

WHITE	BLACK
1. B—B5	Any move
2. Mates accordingly	

•

PUZZLE No. 23

WHITE	BLACK
1. Q—R5	K x P*
2. K x P	Kt x Kt ch
3. K—B3. Mate	

* If Black plays 1. K—B5, then 2. K—K4; if Kt x Kt or Kt—Q7, then 2. R—Q1 ch; if 1. Kt—K3, then 2. Q—B3 ch, mating on the third move in each case.

•

PUZZLE No. 24

WHITE	BLACK
1. K—B8	Kt x B
2. B—B5 ch	K—Q5
3. Kt—R5	Any move
4. Kt mates	

NOTE: This puzzle is a deliberate brain-teaser. The above is the requested four-move solution, but the problem can of course be solved in only three moves.

•

115

PUZZLE No. 25

WHITE	BLACK
1. Kt—KB4	B x Kt (best)
2. B—K4	K x B (best)
3. Q—QB4 ch and mates next move	

•

PUZZLE No. 26

WHITE	BLACK
1. R—K3	Any move
2. Mates accordingly	

•

PUZZLE No. 27

WHITE	BLACK
1. Q—B8	Any move
2. Mates accordingly	

•

PUZZLE No. 28

WHITE	BLACK
1. R—K4	B—Q5*
2. R x P ch	K, P, or B x R
3. Q mates accordingly	

* If Black plays 1. Kt—B5 ch, White replies with 2. K—B7, and if 1. K—K3, then 2. Q—B8 ch, etc.

•

PUZZLE No. 29

WHITE	BLACK
1. Q—Kt8	Any move
2. Mates accordingly	

•

PUZZLE No. 30

WHITE	BLACK
1. B—B2	R—B8*
2. Kt—K5	Any move
3. Mates accordingly	

* Variations on Black's moves should present no difficulty to the player.

•

PUZZLE No. 31

WHITE	BLACK
1. P—K4	P x P*
2. Kt—Q3	Any move
3. Mates accordingly	

* Variations on Black's moves should present no difficulty to the player.

•

PUZZLE No. 32

WHITE	BLACK
1. R—Q5	K x R
2. P—K4	Any move
3. B mates	

•

PUZZLE No. 33

WHITE	BLACK
1. P—K6	Any move
2. Mates accordingly	

•

PUZZLE No. 34

White	Black
1. Q—Kt6	B x Q*
2. B—B6 ch	R—Q4
3. R x R. Mate	

* If Black plays 1. K—Q4, or 1. R x Kt, or 1. Kt x R, or 1. R—Kt5, White continues as above, mating on the third move with Kt, R, or Q, according to the defense adopted. If Black plays 1. K x Kt, then follows 2. Q—Kt2 ch, and 3. P—KB3, discovering ch; if 1. R x P, then 2. R—K6 ch; and if 1. R—K3, then 2. R x R ch, and 3. B or Q mates.

•

PUZZLE No. 35

White	Black
1. P x P ch	K—KR2 (best)
2. Q—KKt7 ch	R x Q
3. Kt from	
Q7—KB6 ch	P x Kt
4. Kt x P. Mate	

•

PUZZLE No. 36

White	Black
1. B—QB1	Any move
2. Mates accordingly	

•

PUZZLE No. 37

White	Black
1. Q—B2	P—B4*
2. Q x RP	K moves
3. Mates by Q—R1 or	
B—K6, accordingly	

* If Black plays 1. P—K3, White continues with 2. B x P ch; if 1. K x Kt or 1. K—K5, then 2. B—K6; and if 1. P—R6, then 2. Kt—Kt6 ch, mating on the third move in each case.

PUZZLE No. 38

White	Black
1. Kt—K4	B x Kt
2. R—Q5 ch	K—B6
3. Q x P. Mate	

•

PUZZLE No. 39

White	Black
1. K—Kt4	Any move
2. Mates accordingly	

•

PUZZLE No. 40

White	Black
1. Q—B5	Kt—B3*
2. K—K4	Any move
3. Mates accordingly	

* If Black plays 1. Kt—QKt4 or 1. Kt—K6, White continues with 2. Q—K6 ch, and mates with Q or Kt on the next move.

•

PUZZLE No. 41

White	Black
1. Q—KB8	K—Q4*
2. Q—B6	K—B4
3. R—Kt5. Mate	

* If Black plays 1. K—K4, then 2. R—Kt5 ch, mating next move with Q or B accordingly.

•

117

PUZZLE No. 42

White	Black
1. B—Q7	K—Q4*
2. Kt—K4	Any move
3. Q—KKt8. Mate	

* If Black plays 1. K x Kt, White continues 2. B—R4 dis ch; and if 1. Kt—B2 or 1. Kt—Kt3, then 2. Q—B7 ch, mating in each case on the third move.

•

PUZZLE No. 43

White	Black
1. Q—KB1	B x Q*.
2. P—Q4 ch	P x P e.p.
3. Kt from Kt6—B4. Mate	

* If 1. K x Kt or 1. Kt—B7, White continues 2. Q—QB4; if 1 Kt x KP, then 2. Q x P ch; if 1. Kt x RP, then 2. Kt—B4 ch, mating in each case on the third move. In the leading variation, if Black on his second move plays K x Kt, 3. Kt—B8 mates.

•

PUZZLE No. 44

White	Black
1. P—Q4	B x P*
2. Q—Kt4	Any move
3. Q mates	

* If Black plays 1. B—K2, White moves K—Kt4 and mates next move with Q.

•

PUZZLE No. 45

White	Black
1. Kt from R4—Kt6	Kt—B2*
2. Kt—B5	Any move
3. Q, R, or Kt mates accordingly	

* If 1. Kt—Kt3, White adopts the continuation set forth above.

•

PUZZLE No. 46

White	Black
1. Q—K7	Any move
2. Mates accordingly	

•

PUZZLE No. 47

White	Black
1. B—QKt6	Any move
2. Mates accordingly	

•

PUZZLE No. 48

White	Black
1. R—KB4 ch	R x R
2. Kt—QB3 ch	P x Kt
3. R x B dis ch	Q x B
4. R x Kt	B—Q5
5. Q—KB5. Mate	

•

PUZZLE No. 49

White	Black
1. Kt x P	P—K3*
2. Kt—QKt5	Any move
3. Kt, R, or B mates	

* If Black plays 1. K x R, then follows 2. B—QB4 ch, and mates next move.

PUZZLE No. 50

White	Black
1. R—R5	P x Q
2. R—Kt2	P moves
3. P—Q5. Mate	

·

PUZZLE No. 51

White	Black
1. B—KB7	P—QKt3 (best)
2. R—K7	K—QB4
3. R—Q7 dis ch	

·

PUZZLE No. 52

White	Black
1. Kt—Kt6	K—B6*
2. B—Kt1	Any move
3. R or B mates accordingly	

* If Black plays 1. K—K4, White continues with 2. B x P, and 3. either B mates.

·

PUZZLE No. 53

White	Black
1. R—QR1	Any move
2. Mates accordingly	

·

PUZZLE No. 54

White	Black
1. K—Kt1	Kt x B*
2. Kt—B3 ch	K moves
3. Q or P mates accordingly	

* If Black plays 1. Kt—Q1, White continues as in the main variation; if any other move, then 2. Q—R1 ch, and 3. Q mates.

PUZZLE No. 55

White	Black
1. Kt x P	R—K3*
2. Kt—B6	Any move
3. Q or Kt mates	

*If Black plays 1. R—B4, White continues with 2. Kt—B2; if 1. R—K1, then 2. Q—B1 ch, etc.; and if 1. B moves, 2. Kt—B6, mating in every case on the third move.

·

PUZZLE No. 56

White	Black
1. Q—K6	Any move
2. Mates accordingly	

·

PUZZLE No. 57

White	Black
1. B—KR4	Any move
2. Mates accordingly	

·

PUZZLE No. 58

White	Black
1. Q—QB1	Any move
2. Mates accordingly	

·

PUZZLE No. 59

White	Black
1. Q—B1	Any move
2. Q, R, or B mates accordingly	

·

PUZZLE No. 60

WHITE	BLACK
1. Kt—K1	K—K4
2. B—B6	K moves
3. Mates accordingly	

●

PUZZLE No. 61

WHITE	BLACK
1. Kt—R5	K—R5
2. Kt—R3	K—Kt5
3. Kt—B2 ch	K—R5
4. P—Kt3. Mate	

●

PUZZLE No. 62

WHITE	BLACK
1. Kt—KB5	Any move
2. Mates accordingly	

●

PUZZLE No. 63

WHITE	BLACK
1. P—QB4	K—Q5*
2. Q—QKt2 ch	K moves
3. Q or Kt mates accordingly	

* Variations arising from Black's play present no difficulty.

●

PUZZLE No. 64

WHITE	BLACK
1. Q—Kt7	R—Q5*
2. Q—KB3	P x Q
3. P—Kt4. Mate	

* The variations springing from Black's play are obvious.

PUZZLE No. 65

WHITE	BLACK
1. Kt—K3	K x Kt*
2. K—Q6	K moves
3. Kt mates accordingly	

* If Black plays 1. K—K4, the continuation is 2. Kt—Q7 ch, etc.

●

PUZZLE No. 66

WHITE	BLACK
1. Q—K1	Any move
2. Mates accordingly	

●

PUZZLE No. 67

WHITE	BLACK
1. Kt—R4	Any move
2. Mates accordingly	

●

PUZZLE No. 68

WHITE	BLACK
1. Kt—QB4	K x R*
2. Q—QB6 ch	K x Q
3. Kt—K7. Mate	

* If Black plays 1. K—B5, the continuation is 2. Kt—K7 ch and 3. Q mates. If 1. Kt—Q3 ch, then 2. Kt x Kt ch, K x R, or B x Kt; 3. Kt—K7 or 3. Kt—B6 mate accordingly. If 1. Kt—KB4, then 2. R x B ch, Kt x R, and Kt—B6 mate. If Kt—Kt4, then 2. R x B ch, K—B5, and 3. P mates. If 1. Kt—B6, then 2. Q—Kt6 ch, and 3. Kt or P mates according to Black's play. If 1. B moves, then 2. Q—Kt6 ch, any move, and 3. R or P mates accordingly.

●

120

PUZZLE No. 69

White	Black
1. Q—QB7 ch	R x Q
2. R—Q6	Q x B (best)
3. P—Q4 ch	K x R
4. P—QB5. Mate	

●

PUZZLE No. 70

White	Black
1. P—K5	K—B5
2. R—QKt1	K—Q5
3. R—K1	K—B5
4. R—K4. Mate	

●

PUZZLE No. 71

White	Black
1. Q—QB1	R—KR3* ** ***
2. Kt—KB5	K—Kt3
3. P—Kt4 ch	R x P
4. Q mates	

*1.	R—KB5
2. Kt—KB5	P x Kt
3. Q x R and mates next move	

**1.	R—KB6
2. Kt—KB5	R—KB5
3. Q x R and mates next move	

***1.	R—KB7
2. P—Kt4 ch	K—Kt4 (best)
3. Kt—Kt2 dis ch	R—B5
4. Q x R. Mate	

●

PUZZLE No. 72

White	Black
1. P—KKt4	P—KR3 (best)
2. Kt—Q2 ch	B x Kt
3. Q x KP ch	K x Q
4. R—Q5 dble ch	K—K3 or K5
5. R—K5. Mate	

●

PUZZLE No. 73

White	Black
1. Q—QB3	R x B (best)
2. Kt—K4	P x P (best)
3. Q—QB6 ch	K x P
4. Q—Q6 ch	K x Kt
5. Kt—Kt5. Mate	

NOTE: The ingenious will have found the above five-move solution to this puzzle, when in fact a three-move solution is possible:

1. Kt—K4 dis ch	K x Kt (best)
2. Q—K5 ch	K—B6
3. Q x P. Mate	

●

PUZZLE No. 74

White	Black

NOTE: Black can make a variety of moves, but given here are only the chief two, as there is no play by which Black can defer the mate beyond four moves.

1. B—K1	Q x Q*
2. P—Q4	P x P e.p.
	[If Q x P, White plays Kt—Kt3 ch and mates with R next move.]
3. Kt—KKt3 ch	Kt—Q5, or K x Kt
4. Kt—K6, mate; or R—KB5, mate	

*1.	R x Q**
2. P—Q3 ch	R, Kt, or P x P
3. Kt—KKt3 ch	K x Kt, or
	K—Q5
4. R—B5, mate;	
or Kt—K6, mate	

**1.	O—KKt2
2. Q—Q4 ch	Q x Q
3. Kt—KKt3 ch	K x Kt
4. R mates	

•

PUZZLE NO. 75

WHITE	BLACK
1. Kt—QB5 dis ch	K—Q3
2. B—K7 ch	K x R
3. R—KKt5	Any move
4. B moves, dis mate	

•

PUZZLE NO. 76

WHITE	BLACK
1. R—K2	R—K1 (best)
2. B—QB8	R—K2
3. R—K5 ch	R x R
4. B—QKt7. Mate	

•

PUZZLE NO. 77

WHITE	BLACK
1. KB—KR3	Q—QR3 ch*
2. Q x Q	B x B, or R—B2
3. R—Q4 dis ch	Any move
4. Q x P. Mate	

* If B x B, or P—Kt3, White replies
with R—Q4, equally forcing mate in
the stipulated number of moves—and
in case of any other mode of defense,
mates sooner.

•

PUZZLE No. 78

WHITE	BLACK
1. Q x Kt	P x Q (best)
2. P—K4	QR—QB6 (best)
3. Kt—K5	QR—QR6*
4. B—QB5, and	
mates with B or	
Kt next move	

* It is evident that Black cannot move
this R from the line it stands on, or
the B will mate at K3; and it is equally
plain that if the other R is moved, Kt x
P, mating.

•

PUZZLE No. 79

WHITE	BLACK
1. R—K5 ch	K—QB5*
2. B—Q5 ch	Kt x B
3. R—K4	Either Kt moves
4. Kt mates at	
K3 or K5	

*1.	K—Q3
2. R—K8 dble ch	Kt—K4
3. B x Kt ch	K—Q2
4. B—QB6. Mate	

•

PUZZLE No. 80

WHITE	BLACK
1. R—K7 ch	B x R
2. P—K4	B x P*
3. KB—QR6	Any move
4. KB mates	

* If Black plays 2. B—KB8, White's
reply is KB x B—and mates next
move.

•

PUZZLE No. 81

WHITE	BLACK
1. B—KB5	P x B (best)
2. K moves	K—QB5
3. B—K3	P—KB5
4. R mates	

•

PUZZLE No. 82

WHITE	BLACK
1. B—K4	P x B
2. Kt x QKtP	P x P (best)
3. R—K5	P moves
4. Kt—QB6. Mate	

•

PUZZLE No. 83

WHITE	BLACK
1. B—QR6	P x Kt (best)*
2. P x P ch	K—Q3
3. Kt—K4 ch	K moves, or
	B x Kt
4. B x KP. Mate	

* If otherwise, White would mate next move.

•

PUZZLE NO. 84

WHITE	BLACK
1. B—K6	P x B
2. R—KKt4	P—K4
3. K—Q7	K—Q4
4. Kt—QB3 ch	K—QB4
5. R—QB4. Mate	

•

PUZZLE No. 85

WHITE	BLACK
1. Q—KR7	K—Q4 (best)
2. Q—K4 ch	K—QB5 (best)
3. Q—QKt7	P—Q4
4. Kt mates	

PUZZLE No. 86

WHITE	BLACK
1. QR x B ch	P x R
2. R—KB3	K moves
3. B—QKt5	K x Kt, or
	K—K3
4. B mates	

•

PUZZLE No. 87

WHITE	BLACK
1. Q—KR1	P—K5 (or Q
	mates at KR7)
2. Q x B	P—K4 (or Q
	mates at KB6)
3. Q—QB8 ch	R interposes
4. Q x Kt	Any move
5. Q—KB1. Mate	

•

PUZZLE No. 88

WHITE	BLACK
1. R—Q4 ch	P x R
2. R—QB6 ch	K—Q4
3. Kt—K6	R—Q2 or Q3
4. Kt x QBP. Mate	

•

PUZZLE No. 89

WHITE	BLACK
1. Kt—QB4 dble ch	K—Q4 (best)
2. Q—KR1 ch	K x Kt (best)
3. K—QKt7	B—QKt4*
4. Q—K4. Mate	

* If Black played B—QR5, this move would delay the mate one more move.

•

PUZZLE No. 90

WHITE	BLACK
1. R—QKt7	Q—K2 (best)
2. Q—QB6 ch	R—QB2
3. R—QKt8 ch	K x R
4. Q mates	

●

PUZZLE No. 91

WHITE	BLACK
1. Kt—KB6	B x Kt*
2. Q—QB8	R x Q (best)
3. R—Q6	B—Q4
4. K—K3	Q x QBP
5. B—KR2. Mate	

*1.	B x Q
2. P—KB4	P x P
3. Kt—KB3. Mate	

●

PUZZLE No. 92

WHITE	BLACK
1. Q—KB4	P—K4 (best)
2. Q—QB1	Q—KKt4*
3. B—KKt6 dis ch	Q x Q
4. B—K8 and	
mates next move	

*2.	Kt—QKt3
3. B—Q3 dis ch	R—QB7
4. Q x R, and	
mates next move	

●

PUZZLE No. 93

WHITE	BLACK
1. Kt x Kt	P—B8, queens (best)
2. B—K7 ch	K x Kt
3. Q—KKt6 ch	Q interposes
4. Q x Q. Mate	

●

PUZZLE No. 94

WHITE	BLACK
1. R—KB7	P—QR3*
2. R—KB3	P—QR4
3. K—QB3	K x Kt
4. B mates	

*1.	P—QR4
2. B—QKt5	K x P
3. B mates	

●

PUZZLE No. 95

WHITE	BLACK
1. R—QR1	P—QB4** ***
2. R—R4	P x Kt*
3. Kt x P,	
and B dis ch and	
mates next move	

* If Black plays 2. P x B, the reply is
3. R—R6 and mates next move.

**1.	P—QR4
2. R—R4	P x B
3. R x P ch	K moves
4. Kt—QKt3. Mate	

***1.	Kt—KB3
2. R—R4	Kt—K5 ch
3. K—K3	Kt attacks R
4. Kt—R3. Mate	

●

PUZZLE No. 96

WHITE	BLACK
1. Q—K7 ch	K x Q
2. P—K5	R—QB3 (best)
3. Kt—KB6 dis ch	R x R
4. P—K8. Mate	

●

PUZZLE No. 97

WHITE	BLACK
1. B—KB1	P moves
2. P—QR3	P moves
3. Kt—Q3	K x P
4. K—B1	K moves
5. Kt mates	

●

PUZZLE No. 98

WHITE	BLACK
1. R from KB5—QKt5	K moves*
2. R—QKt7 ch	Any move
3. R or Kt mates	

*1.	R—K7
2. R x QRP	Any move
3. R or Kt mates	

●

PUZZLE No. 99

WHITE	BLACK
1. Q—K4 ch	K—B3
2. Q—KB4 ch	K—K2 (best)
3. Q—KB7 ch	K—K3
4. Kt from B5 x P ch	K moves
5. Kt—QB6 ch	K moves
6. Q—KB3. Mate	

●

PUZZLE No. 100

WHITE	BLACK
1. B—KB6 ch	K x R*
2. Kt—K5	K—Q5 (best)
3. Kt—KKt4 dis ch	K x P
4. Kt mates	

*1.	K x P
2. R—QB3 ch	K—Q4
3. R x P ch	R x R
4. Kt mates	

PUZZLE No. 101

WHITE	BLACK
1. B—KR4 ch	R x B (best)
2. Q—QR7	K x R*
3. Kt—K6 dis ch	K—Kt1, or R1, or B3, or Kt3, or R3
4. Q—KKt7. Mate	

*2.	Any other move
3. Kt—K8 ch	R x Kt
4. Q—KB7. Mate	

●

PUZZLE No. 102

WHITE	BLACK
1. P—QB3 ch	K x B
2. Kt—QB5 ch	K x Kt
3. R—KB5	K x Kt
4. R x Kt. Mate	

●

PUZZLE No. 103

WHITE	BLACK
1. Kt—KB5	Kt—QB1 (best)
2. B—Q4	P—Q3 (best)
3. B—QB5	P x B (best)*
4. R—K4	Any move
5. R mates	

*3.	P—KR7
4. B x QP	Any move
5. R or Kt mates	

●

PUZZLE No. 104

WHITE	BLACK
1. Kt x B	P x Kt (best)
2. R—QB1	P moves
3. R—KB1	P moves
4. R—KB5	P x R
5. B mates	

●

PUZZLE No. 105

WHITE	BLACK
1. Q—Q1	P x B*
2. P—Q4	P x P e.p.
3. Q—KR5 ch	K moves
4. Q—K5. Mate	

*1.	K—KB4**
2. Q—KR5 ch	K—QKt3
3. B x P ch, and	
mates next move	

**1.	Q—K7
2. Q x Q	K—QB4
3. B x P ch and	
mates next move	

•

PUZZLE No. 106

WHITE	BLACK
1. R—KKt3	K—B5* **
2. Q—Q3	P x Q
3. B—QB6, and	
mates next move	

*1.	P—K4
2. B—KKt5	Any move
3. White mates	
obviously in two	
moves	

** If Black plays 1. Kt—QB6, then
White answers with 2. B x P ch, and
mates in two more moves. Again, if
Black plays 1. R—Q2, the reply is 2.
Q—KKt8, 3. Q—Kt5 ch, 4. Q x P and
mates.

•

PUZZLE No. 107

WHITE	BLACK
1. Q—QR5	QKt x Kt (best)
2. Q—K8	KKt—Q2
3. Q—KKt5 ch	R x Q
4. P—Q4. Mate	

PUZZLE No. 108

WHITE	BLACK
1. Kt x R ch	R x Kt
2. Q—KKt5	R—K4 ch*
3. K—B6	Kt—K5 ch
4. P x Kt ch	K x P
5. Q x R. Mate	

* Black may play instead 2. Q—QB1,
or 2. P—QB4, but the mate is equally
forced in the same number of moves.

•

PUZZLE No. 109

WHITE	BLACK
1. R—K4	R x B (best)
2. Kt x P ch	K—K3
3. Kt—Q4 ch	K—K2
4. B x Kt dble ch	K x B (best)
5. R—K5 and	
mates next move	

•

PUZZLE No. 110

WHITE	BLACK
1. R—QB4 ch	K x R*
2. Kt—K3 ch	K—QB4
3. B—K5	B moves
4. P—Q4. Mate	

*1.	B x R
2. P—Q4 ch	K—Q3
3. B—K5 ch	K—Q4
4. Kt—QB3. Mate	

•

PUZZLE No. 111

White	Black
1. R x R	Q—K1*
2. Kt from	
K5—Q7 ch	K x Kt
3. Kt x Kt ch	Q x Kt
4. Q—K5. Mate	
*1.	R—KB6 ch
2. Q x R ch	K x Q
3. R—KB7. Mate	

PUZZLE No. 112

White	Black
1. Q—QR3	Kt x P*
2. Q—KB3	Any move
3. Q, B, or P mates	
*1.	K x P [If any other move, then Q x Kt and mates next move.]
2. Q x Kt ch and mates next move	

PUZZLE No. 113

White	Black
1. Kt—KB1 ch	K—K7*
2. Q—Q6**	R—Q6 (best)
3. Kt—K6	R—KB1
4. Q x R ch	B x Q
5. Kt mates	

* If either P takes Q, then Kt—K6, and mate follows next move.

**If White plays 2. Kt—K6 instead of Q—Q6, Black answers with P—QB4, and, on White playing Q x QBP, Black checks with Q, etc.

PUZZLE No. 114

White	Black
1. R x B ch	B x R
2. Q—QR1 ch	Q—QB6
3. Q—QR7 ch	Kt—QB4
4. Q—KKt7 ch	R x Q
5. Kt—KB5. Mate	

PUZZLE No. 115

White	Black
1. B—Q6 ch	K—R1 (best)
2. B—K5	P—KB7 (best)
3. P queens	P queens ch
4. K—QKt2	Q—QKt8 ch (best)
5. Q x Q	Q x Q
6. B—K4 ch	Q—QB3
7. B x Q. Mate	

PUZZLE No. 116

White	Black
1. R—QKt7	Q x Q
2. B—K4	Q—Q5*
3. Kt x Q	Any move
4. R—QKt1 dis ch	

* Black has other moves, but none which can possibly retard the mate.

PUZZLE No. 117

White	Black
1. Q—KR4 ch	K—K3
2. Q—KR6 ch	K—Q2 (best)
3. B x P ch	K—Q1
4. Q x P ch	P x Q
5. B—QKt6. Mate	

PUZZLE No. 118

White	Black
1. B—QB6	K x Kt (best)
2. K—K5	P x P
3. B—KB3	P—QB3
4. B—K2	P x B
5. P—Q4. Mate	

PUZZLE No. 119

White	Black
1. B—KR7 ch	Kt—KB4
2. B—QKt2	Q—K4
3. Kt x Q	R—QR1
4. Kt—Q7	R—KB1
5. Kt—QB5 ch	P x Kt
6. R mates	

PUZZLE No. 120

White	Black
1. K—K3	P—QB4
2. Kt—QR5	P—QB5
3. P x P ch and mate	

PUZZLE No. 121

White	Black
1. Kt—Q7	R at QB2 x Kt*
2. B—Q1	R x B (best)
3. B—Kt	Kt x B**
4. R—Kt4 ch and Q mates	

*1.	R at Q1 x Kt [Any other move than taking Kt accelerates the mate.]
2. B—K7	R x B
3. B—Q1 and mates in two more moves	

**If any other move, then 4. Q—KKt4 ch, and 5. B x P. Mates.

PUZZLE No. 122

White	Black
1. Kt—K5 dis ch	K—Kt8
2. Kt at K5—QB6	Q x Kt
3. B—QB5	Q x B*
4. Q—KKt8 ch	K—R8
5. R—KB1. Mate	

*3.	Q x Q
4. Kt—K2 dble ch	K—R8
5. R—KB1. Mate	

PUZZLE No. 123

White	Black
1. Q—KB2	R—QKt2*
2. Q x B	Q—Q5 (best)
3. Q x QP**	Q—KB8 (best)
4. Kt—KB2 ch	Q x Kt
5. Q—KR2. Mate	

*1.	R—Q2***
2. Q x R	Q—Q5 (best)
3. Q x Q	R—KB8
4. Q—KKt1 ch	R x Q
5. Kt—KB2. Mate	

** If White plays Q x Q, Black will play R—QKt7.

*** If Black plays 1. Q—KR4, then follows 2. B x Q, etc.

PUZZLE No. 124

White	Black
1. Kt—KB5 ch	K x P*
2. Q—QR2 ch	K x Kt
3. Kt—KKt3 ch	K x P
4. Q—Q2 ch	K x Kt
5. Q—KR2 ch. Mate	

*1.	K—K1
2. Kt—Kt7 ch	K—K2
3. Q—QKt4 ch	P—QB4
4. Q x P ch	B—Q3
5. Q x B ch. Mate	

PUZZLE No. 125

WHITE	BLACK
1. R x QP ch	K x R (best)
2. Kt—QKt4 ch	K—K4
3. R—Q3 ch	Q x B
4. R—Q5 ch	R x R
5. Kt—B6. Mate	

•

PUZZLE No. 126

WHITE	BLACK
1. R—K6	P queens*
2. Kt—Kt6 ch	P x Kt
3. R—QR5	P x R
4. R mates	

* Black has many other moves, but none better than this.

•

PUZZLE No. 127

WHITE	BLACK
1. KB—KB5 ch	Q x B*
2. Kt—QB5 ch	K x B
3. Kt—K6 dble ch	K moves
4. Q—Q4 ch	R x Q
5. Kt—QB5. Mate	

*1.	K x B
2. Kt—Q6 ch	K—K3
3. P—KB5 ch	K—K2
4. Kt—QB8 ch	K moves
5. Q x Q. Mate	

•

PUZZLE No. 128

WHITE	BLACK
1. Q—Q2 ch	K x Kt on K5*
2. Kt—KR6	Any move
3. Q or Kt mates	

*1.	K x the other Kt
2. P—KKt4 ch	K x Kt
3. Q—KR2. Mate	

PUZZLE No. 129

WHITE	BLACK
1. Kt—K6	P x R (best)
2. P—KR6	P—KKt4
3. Kt—QB7	P or K moves
4. Kt—Q5. Mate	

•

PUZZLE No. 130

WHITE	BLACK
1. Kt—QB2	K—Q4*
2. R x QBP	K x R**
3. Q—QB6. Mate	

* If B or P x Kt, then follow 2. R x QBP and 3. Q mates.

**If any other move, Q mates at K6.

•

PUZZLE No. 131

WHITE	BLACK
1. QP x Kt	Kt—K4 (best)
2. Q x KRP	Kt—Q6*
3. Q—K8	Any move
4. Q mates	

*2.	Kt x P
3. Kt—K6	Any move
4. Q mates	

•

PUZZLE No. 132

WHITE	BLACK
1. R—KR4	Kt—K6*
2. R—KR4	K or P moves
3. R mates	

*1.	K—QB6
2. R—R2	Any move
3. Q mates	

•

PUZZLE No. 133

White	Black
1. B—KKt3	P—KB2*
2. Kt—KB4 dis ch	K—K4, QB4, QB6, or K x Kt
3. R or Kt mates	
*1.	P—QKt6**
2. Kt—KB4 ch	K—QB6
3. B—K1. Mate	

**If K—QB4, then follow 2. Kt—QB7, and mate next move.

•

PUZZLE No. 134

White	Black
1. R x P ch	K x R (best)
2. Kt—Q4	K x Kt*
3. Q—Q5. Mate	

* If any other moves, then White plays 3. Q—QB3 or Q—QKt3. Mate.

•

PUZZLE No. 135

White	Black
1. Q—KKt1 ch	Q x Q (best)
2. B—Q6 ch	B x B
3. R—K5 ch	B x R
4. Kt—K6 ch	K—Q4
5. P—QB4. Mate	

•

PUZZLE No. 136

White	Black
1. Kt—Q4	Kt from R6—B5 (best)
2. K—Kt3	Kt—Q8 (best)
3. Q x Kt	P x Q (best)
4. K—B4	Any move
5. K moves and dis ch	

PUZZLE No. 137

White	Black
1. Kt x P	Kt x P (best)*
2. Kt—Q5	K—QB4**
3. Q—QKt1	Any move
4. Q mates	

* If Black plays 1. B x P, White moves either Kt—Q5 or Kt—QR4.

**2.	K—K7
3. Q—QB1	Any move
4. QR or Kt gives mate	

•

PUZZLE No. 138

White	Black
1. R—KR2	Kt x R (best)
2. Q—Q4 and White mates evidently in two more moves.	Any move

•

PUZZLE No. 139

White	Black
1. Q—Q2	R on Q1 x Q (best)
2. B—QB2 ch	Any move
3. Mate	

NOTE: If either Kt takes Q, White may give check with B at QB2 and mate next move with Kt or B.

•

130

PUZZLE No. 140

White	Black
1. KKt—KB3	P x QKt*
2. B—K8	P—QKt8
	becoming Q**
3. Q—K4 ch	K x Q
4. B—QB5. Mate	

* Black has a variety of moves at command, but none by which the mate can be delayed.

** Again Black has a great choice of moves, but play as Black may, mate follows in the four moves.

•

PUZZLE No. 141

White	Black
1. R—QKt7	B—KB2 or
	Kt—KB7
2. Kt—QR7	B x Q*
3. Kt—QR6	Any move
4. Kt mates	

*2.	B—K3 or
	B x P ch
3. Kt x B	Any move
4. Kt mates	

•

PUZZLE No. 142

White	Black
1. B—QKt4	Any move
2. R x P ch and	
mates next move	

PUZZLE No. 143

White	Black
1. Q—QR4 ch	K x R
2. Kt—QKt2 dis ch	K—QKt6
3. Q—QR4 ch	K x Kt
4. R—QR1	K x R (best)
5. Q—QB7 and	
mates next move	

•

PUZZLE No. 144

White	Black
1. Q—KB7	R—K4* **
2. Q—KB4 ch	K x Kt (best)
3. Q—QB4 ch	K x Q
4. Kt mates	

* If 1. K x Kt, then follows 2. Kt—Q6 ch, etc.

**1.	B—KB3
2. Q x R ch	B—K4
3. Kt—KB6 ch	K moves
4. Mates	

•

PUZZLE No. 145

White	Black
1. KB—QB4	P x B (best)
2. R—K2	K moves
3. Kt or P mates	

•

PUZZLE No. 146

White	Black
1. Q—Q3 ch	K—KB6
2. Q—K2 ch	K—K5
3. Q—Q1	Any move
4. Q mates	

•

PUZZLE No. 147

WHITE	BLACK
1. B—KR4	Q—KKt1*
2. Q x KP ch	Kt x Q (best)**
3. B—K1	

* Black may also play 1. Kt—B5 ch, whereupon White plays Kt x Kt and mates in two more moves.

**Although Black can give check with four different pieces, White mates next move.

•

PUZZLE No. 148

WHITE	BLACK
1. R—QKt5	P—QB4*
2. B—QR8	B x B (best)
3. R—QKt1 and mates next move	

* If B x B, then White plays 2. R x B, 3. R x KKtP, 4. R mates. If P—QB3, White plays 2. B x B ch, 3. R x KKtP, etc.

•

PUZZLE No. 149

WHITE	BLACK
1. B—Q1	K—Q5
2. B—QKt3	K—K4*
3. P—K3	P x B
4. P—Q4. Mate	

*2.	P x B
3. R—KB5	K—QB5
4. R—KB4. Mate	

•

PUZZLE No. 150

WHITE	BLACK
1. B—KR7	P—KB4*
2. R x KBP	K—Q6**
3. R—KB3. Mate	

* If Black plays either P one step, R x KBP and gives mate next move.

** 2.	K—K5***
3. R—K5. Mate	

*** If 2. Kt or P moves, then follows R—B3 or R—K5. Mate.

•

PUZZLE No. 151

WHITE	BLACK
1. B—Q8 ch	R—K2
2. Kt—QB3	K x R (best)
3. Kt—K6 dis ch	K—KB3
4. Kt—KKt5	Any move
5. R mates	

•

PUZZLE No. 152

WHITE	BLACK
1. R—QB	Kt—KKt3*
2. Q x R	Q x Q
3. P—KR8 (becomes K)	Kt x Kt (best)
4. R x Kt at Q4	P x Kt
5. R—Q5. Mate	

* There are many choices for Black's first and second moves, but none that can prolong the mate beyond the given number of moves.

•

PUZZLE No. 153

WHITE	BLACK
1. B—KKt4	P—KR3 or KR4
2. B—Q1	P—KR4 or KR5*
3. B—QR4	P moves**
4. Kt—Q3	K moves
5. R mates	

* Or any other move except playing K.

**3.	K—Q3
4. K—Q4	Any move
5. R mates	

•

PUZZLE No. 154

WHITE	BLACK
1. P—QB3	Kt x R*
2. Kt—KR3 and mates next move	

*1.	Kt checks
2. K—K7	Any move
3. R—K3. Mate	

•

PUZZLE No. 155

WHITE	BLACK
1. B—KR8	P—QKt5*
2. Q—KKt7	Any move
3. Q mates	

*1.	R—QR1
2. Q—QB3 and mates next move	

•

PUZZLE No. 156

WHITE	BLACK
1. B—QB1	Black has no choice of moves.
2. B—KR6	
3. B—KB8	
4. B—QB5 ch	
5. Kt mates	

•

PUZZLE No. 157

WHITE	BLACK
1. B—KKt7	R x B (best)
2. R from R2—KB2	Any move
3. R—KKt5, or R—KB4, according as Black plays, giving mate	

•

PUZZLE No. 158

WHITE	BLACK
1. Q—QKt8	K—K4*
2. Kt—K6 dis ch	K—B4
3. B—K4 ch	K x B
4. Q—KB4 ch	K x P
5. Kt—QB7. Mate	

* If Black plays 1. B—KR7, then follows 2. Kt—QKt5 ch, 3. Q x B, etc.

•

PUZZLE No. 159

White	Black
1. B—KKt8	R—Q4 (best)
2. QB—Q8	R x B*
3. Kt—KB6	Any move
4. Kt mates at whichever square Black leaves unguarded.	

* 2.	R—QKt2**
3. P x R	Any move
4. QB mates	

** If R—QB2, QB x R and mates next move.

•

PUZZLE No. 160

White	Black
1. Kt—K2	P x Kt (best)
2. B—QB8	B moves (best)
3. R—Q7	Any move
4. Mates accordingly	

•

PUZZLE No. 161

White	Black
1. R—KB2	P—KB4 or Kt—KKt3
2. Q—Q7	Any move
3. Q or Kt gives mate	

•

PUZZLE No. 162

White	Black
1. K—KR3	K—KR3 (best)
2. K—KKt4 dis ch	K—Kt2
3. R x B ch	K x R
4. Q—KB7 ch	K moves
5. R—KR2. Mate	

•

PUZZLE No . 163

White	Black
1. K—K2	Any P moves
2. B—KRl	Any P moves
3. P—K4	Any move
4. P—K5. Mate	

•

PUZZLE No. 164

White	Black
1. P—QKt5	B x P*
2. Q—QR3	K x R or any move
3. Q—K7. Mate	

* If Black plays KB anywhere, White either takes B, giving mate, or mates by Q x KKtP. If Black plays 1. R—QR8 to prevent 2. Q—QR3, White's reply is 2. R—K8, etc .

•

PUZZLE No. 165

White	Black
1. R—K6 ch	B x R
2. R—Q4 ch	K x R (best)
3. Kt—QB6 ch	K x Kt*
4. B—KB3. Mate	

* If K—K4, then follows 4. Kt—QB3. Mate.

•

PUZZLE No. 166

White	Black
1. Q—QR8	R x Q
2. B—QKt4	R—Q1 ch
3. Kt—Q7 dble ch and mate.	

•

PUZZLE No. 167

WHITE	BLACK
1. K—QKt4	R—KB1 or B—Q1*
2. P—QB4	K x Kt
3. R—Q1 ch	B—Q6
4. R x B ch	K x R
5. R—Q2. Mate	

*1.	K x Kt**
2. R—Q2 ch	B—Q6
3. R x B. Mate	

** Black may also play B—Q6 or B—KB6, but mate can then be given more speedily.

•

PUZZLE No. 168

WHITE	BLACK
1. B—QR3	B—KKt6*
2. B—QB1 ch	B—KB5
3. R x B	Any move
4. R mates	

*1.	K x Kt
2. B—QB1 ch	B—KKt4
3. R—KB4	Any move
4. R mates	

•

PUZZLE No. 169

WHITE	BLACK
1. R—KKt5	R—K1*
2. R x KBP	Any move
3. Q, R, B, or Kt mates	

*1.	R—KB1**
2. Q x R at K5	Any move
3. Q, B, or Kt mates	

**1.	Q ch
2. Kt x Q ch	Kt x Kt
3. Q—Q8. Mate	

PUZZLE No. 170

WHITE	BLACK
1. Kt—Q6 ch	K—K3
2. Kt—KB3	B x P (best)
3. P x B	Q—KKt8 (best)
4. K—Q8	Any move
5. B, Kt, or P mates	

•

PUZZLE No. 171

WHITE	BLACK
1. R—QKt4	P—R7*
2. Q—K3 ch	P x Q
3. Kt—K5 dis ch	

*1.	K—Q6
2. K—Q5	Any move
3. Q mates	

•

PUZZLE No. 172

WHITE	BLACK
1. Kt—QKt6 ch	K moves
2. Q—QB3	B x Q*
3. Kt—Q7 or QR4 ch	K moves
4. Kt mates	

*2.	P—Q4
3. B—K7	K moves
4. Kt mates	

•

PUZZLE No. 173

WHITE	BLACK
1. Q—QB5	Kt—QB7
2. Q—K7	P—KKt5 (best)
3. P—KR4	Q—KB4 or any move
4. Kt x QP ch	Q or R x Kt
5. Q or Kt mates	

•

PUZZLE No. 174

White	Black
1. Q—KKt1	K—K5**
2. B—QB3	K—Q6*
3. B—Q7	K moves
4. B or Q mates	

* If any other move, White plays 3. Q—Q4.

**1.	K—K3 or K4***
2. Q—QB5 and	
mates next move	

***1.	K—Q3
2. Q—K3	K moves
3. B—QB3 or	
KKt4 and mates	
next move	

•

PUZZLE No. 175

White	Black
1. Kt—Q5	B—K4 (best)
2. Q—KB4 ch	K x Kt (best)
3. Q—QB4 ch	K x Q
4. B mates	

•

PUZZLE No. 176

White	Black
1. P—KKt3 ch	K moves
2. Q—KKt6 ch	K x Q
3. Kt—K5 ch	K—R2*
4. P—KB8, be-	
coming Kt ch	K—KR1
5. Kt from K5—KKt6.	
Mate	

* If K—B3, then follows Kt—K4 ch, and P mates. If K—KR5, then P—Kt4 ch, and Kt mates.

•

PUZZLE No. 177

White	Black
1. Q—KKt3	B—Q7*
2. Q—QKt8	B—QKt5
3. Q—KKt8. Mate	

* If Black plays B—QR4, White plays K x B, and Q mates.

•

PUZZLE No. 178

White	Black
1. Kt—K8	P—QB6 (best)
2. P—KB5	K—K4 or K5*
3. R—K6 ch	K moves
4. Kt—KKt7 or	
QB7 ch	K moves
5. R—K4. Mate	

*2.	K—QB5
3. Kt—QB7	K moves
4. R—QR6	K moves
5. R—QR4. Mate	

•

PUZZLE No. 179

White	Black
1. P—KKt6	P x P
2. R—KKt5	P x B
3. P—KB3	P x Kt
4. R—Q5. Mate	

•

PUZZLE No. 180

White	Black
1. R—KB3	K—K4*
2. Q—Q4 ch	K x Q
3. R—K3	Any move
4. R or B mates	

*1.	Kt x R
2. Q—QKt1 ch	K—K4
3. Q—Q4. Mate	

PUZZLE No. 181

White	Black
1. Kt—QKt5 ch	K x R
2. Q—KB5 ch	K x Q
3. Kt—Q4, dble ch and mate	

•

PUZZLE No. 182

White	Black
1. Q—KR8	P—K5 (best)* ** ***
2. Kt—QB6 ch	Kt x Kt
3. Q—QR1. Mate	

*1.	B x B or R x R
2. Q x Kt ch	K moves
3. Q or Kt mates accordingly	

**1.	P—Q7
2. Q—Q8 ch	K moves or interposes Kt
3. Kt or Q mates accordingly	

***1.	Kt—QB3
2. Q—QR8 ch	K moves
3. Kt mates	

•

PUZZLE No. 183

White	Black
1. Q—QKt5	K x P*
2. B—K5 ch	K—K5
3. B—Q6	Any move
4. Q mates	

* 1.	K x B**
2. P—KR4	B x P or K—Kt5
3. Q—KKt5 ch and mates next move	

** If B x P, White plays B—KKt3, mating next move.

PUZZLE No. 184

White	Black
1. Kt—KB8	Any move
2. Kt—K6	Any move
3. Kt mates at KKt5, KB4, or Q4	

•

PUZZLE No. 185

White	Black
1. Kt from QB4—K5	K—QB4*
2. P—QB4	P or R moves
3. R x R or P x P. Mate	

*1.	K—K3**
2. R—Q3	R—K4 or Q4
3. R or B mates	

**If any other move, White checks with R at Q3 or QKt5 and mates with B or P next move.

•

PUZZLE No. 186

White	Black
1. Q—QB5 ch	K x R (best)
2. Q x KBP ch	K x B (best)
3. B—KR3	Any move
4. Q—Q7 or KB8 and mates according as Black moves.	

•

PUZZLE No. 187

White	Black
1. B—KR4	P x B
2. P—Q5	P x QP
3. Kt—KB4	P moves
4. Kt—Q5	Any move
5. K x P. Mate	

•

PUZZLE No. 188

WHITE	BLACK
1. Q x Q	B x Q
2. B—QKt8	Kt—KR2
3. B—KR3	R x B
4. R x P ch	P x R
5. B—KKt3	Any move
6. Kt or P mates	

•

PUZZLE No. 189

WHITE	BLACK
1. Kt—KB2	P x Kt
2. P—Q4	K x R
3. P—K4 dis ch and mate	

•

PUZZLE No. 190

WHITE	BLACK
1. P—Q3 ch	Q—QB5
2. B—KB2	P x B
3. B—KB1	Any move
4. R—KKt7 and mates next move	

•

PUZZLE No. 191

WHITE	BLACK
1. Q—KKt3	P—Q6*
2. Q—QB7	Any move
3. Kt or Q mates	

*1.	Q—KKt1
2. Kt—QKt ch	K—Q7
3. Q mates	

•

PUZZLE No. 192

WHITE	BLACK
1. R—Q4	B x R* **
2. B x P ch	Any move
3. Q mates	

* If K x R, White evidently gives mate next move.

**1.	B x Kt***
2. Q x B ch	K—KB3
3. B—KR4. Mate	

***1.	P x R
2. R—Q5 ch	Any move
3. Q mates	

•

PUZZLE No. 193

WHITE	BLACK
1. Q—QB5 ch	K—Q2**
2. Kt—KB6 ch	K—K3
3. Q x KBP ch	K x Q*
4. B—KR3. Mate	

* If 3. K—K2, then follows 4. Q—Q7. Mate.

**1.	K x Q
2. Kt—QKt4, mating with QP next move.	

•

PUZZLE No. 194

White	Black
1. R—KB5 dis ch	Kt x Q*
2. R—Q5	Q—QR4 (best)
3. Kt—QKt5 dis ch	Q—Q7
4. Kt mates	

*1.	K—Q7**
2. Q—K2 ch	K—QB6
3. Kt—QKt5 ch	R or B x Kt
4. R or B mates	

**1.	R—KB6
2. Q x R ch	K—Q7
3. Q x P ch	K x Q
4. B—QB1. Mate	

•

PUZZLE No. 195

White	Black
1. Q x QP ch	R from Q8 x Q (best)
2. R—QR5	Any move
3. Mates according to Black's play	

•

PUZZLE No. 196

White	Black
1. R—KKt7	Kt—KB2 (best)
2. R x KtP	Kt x R (best)
3. B—KKt7 ch	Kt x B
4. Kt—QB6	Kt moves
5. Kt mates at KB5 or KB7	

•

PUZZLE No. 197

White	Black
1. B—KB5	K—KB3
2. R—QR1	K—Kt4*
3. Kt—K4 ch	K moves
4. R mates	

*2.	K—K2
3. R—QR7 ch	K moves
4. R or Kt mates	

•

PUZZLE No. 198

White	Black
1. Kt x QP	KtP x P or R—Q2*
2. P—K3 ch	
3. P—QB3 and mates next move	

*If Black plays 1. B x Kt, then follows R x B and R—QB5, mating next move. If 1. R x Kt, or 1. Kt—QB4, White checks with KP and then plays Kt—QB7 dis ch, etc. And, finally, if 1. B—QB6 ch, White captures Kt with Kt, in every case giving mate in four moves.

•

PUZZLE No. 199

White	Black
1. R—Q4	K x R*
2. Q—K3 ch	K x Q
3. Kt—QB4. Mate	

*1.	Q—K3**
2. Q x Q	Kt or K x R or Kt—QB3
3. Kt—Q3 or Kt—Q7. Mate	

** If Black plays 1. Q or Kt x R, then follows 2. B—KB8 ch and 3. Q or B mates. If Black plays 1. Q—QB3, then ensues 2. Q x Q ch and 3. Kt—Q7 or Kt—QB4. Mate.

PUZZLE No. 200

	WHITE	BLACK
1.	Kt—K4 dis ch	K—B4 (best)
2.	R—KB6 ch	*
3.	R—KR6 dis ch	
4.	Kt—KKt3 ch	
5.	Kt x B ch	
6.	R—KB6 ch	
7.	R x QKtP dis ch	
8.	R—KB6 ch	
9.	R—QB6 dis ch	
10.	Kt—KKt3 ch	
11.	Kt—K2 ch	
12.	Q—KKt6 ch	
13.	R x QBP ch	
14.	P mates	

* After first move, Black's moves are forced.

NOTE: The ingenious will have discovered that this puzzle can also be solved in twelve moves.

•

140

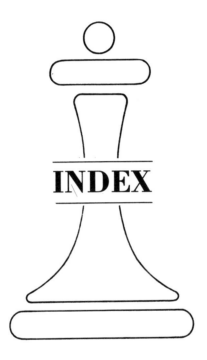

INDEX

INDEX

References are to puzzle number and not to page